ISBN
979-8-9859964-0-1 (Electronic)
979-8-9859964-1-8 (Hardcover)
979-8-9859964-2-5 (So' cover)

Book edited by Book elpline
https://bookhelpli e.com

Book Helpline is committed to helping authors fulfill their writing
ambitions.

D1260540

CONTENTS

ABOUT THE AUTHOR

Dr. Yoav Wachsman is a professor of economics at Coastal Carolina University. He completed his undergraduate degree in economics with minors in history, psychology, and philosophy from Salisbury University in Maryland. He received his Ph.D. in economics from the University of Hawai'i at Mānoa.

Dr. Wachsman specializes in environmental economics and the economics of tourism. He has published research papers in environmental economics and has written several reports on sustainable development for organizations and local governments. Dr. Wachsman has a keen interest in sustainable development and sustainable energy. He helped develop the environmental sustainability minor at Coastal Carolina University and presented several talks about the importance of sustainable development and shifting to sustainable energy.

Before becoming a professor, Dr. Wachsman worked at the National Marine and Fisheries Services in Honolulu, Hawaii. His research examined how to regulate fisheries to achieve long-term sustainability. He believes that good environmental stewardship is imperative for nature and paramount for our economic well-being. He is an educator, economist, and environmentalist.

Yoav Wachsman, Ph.D.

FOR MY SON

At the beginning of 2022, I became a father for the first time. When I hold my son, I know I will do what I can to ensure that he has a bright and healthy future.

As an educator, I must help assure that my son grows up in a future with a healthy environment, a stable climate, and a strong economy. Fossil fuels have no place in his future. As this book explains, fossil fuels degrade the environment, create climatic instability, and destabilize our economy. Money from fossil fuels empowers rogue nations and terrorist organizations.

I hope Bryce grows up on a planet where we no longer use oil, coal, or natural gas. Instead, we empower vehicles using electricity generated from sustainable sources. We must ensure that our children grow in a sustainable world and that our children's future is electric.

INTRODUCTION: RUNNING OUT OF GAS

If you change the way you look at things, the things you look at change. Wayne Dyer

Before 2021, few Americans had heard about Colonial Pipeline, even though its pipelines supply around 45% of the Eastern Seaboard fuel. However, on May 7, 2021, Colonial Pipeline was in the headlines when it announced that a group of computer hackers called Darkside had breached its security and planted ransomware in its system. Ransomware is a nasty malware that infiltrates data systems and encrypts their information. Hackers typically demand a hefty ransom in cryptocurrency to decrypt the information. They usually threaten to destroy data or release it to the public if the company does not pay.

Colonial Pipeline caved quickly and paid $4.4 million. Yet, it took six days to turn its supply lines back on. With each passing day, the public became increasingly anxious about the availability of gasoline. The shutdown led to a surge in gas prices and panic buying, leaving hundreds of gas stations around the Southeast without gas. By Wednesday, May 12, 70% of the gas stations in North Carolina were out of gas. Many drivers followed social media posts to find out where gasoline was available. Some drivers went beyond filling their gas tanks. They filled gas cans, canisters, and even plastic bags with gasoline in a rush to get as much gasoline as possible.

The vexing scene that followed the cyberattack on Colonial Pipeline demonstrates two things. First, we have become overly reliant on gasoline. Secondly, since we rely on gasoline, we are susceptible to supply shocks. The global gasoline supply is vulnerable to natural disasters, wars, political manipulations, financial speculations, and cyberattacks. The USA experienced widespread gasoline shortages during the Organization of Petroleum Exporting Countries (OPEC) crises in 1973, the Persian Gulf War in 1990, the energy crisis in 2008, the Deepwater Horizon spill in 2010, and the Russian invasion of Ukraine in 2022. These supply shocks raised the price of gasoline, created inflationary pressure, and disrupted the global economy.

In addition to making us vulnerable to supply shocks, petroleum and other fossil fuels like natural gas and coal lead to habitat destruction, air pollution, water pollution, and climatic instability. Burning fossil fuels releases greenhouse gases like carbon dioxide and methane, which trap heat in the earth's atmosphere. Articles, books, and videos explain how greenhouse gases work. A simple explanation is that greenhouse gases act like car windows on a sunny day. They let light through but trap the heat. Consequently, the inside of the car can get dangerously hot even when the temperature outside is moderate.

This book uses the term climatic instability instead of the more commonly used but misleading term global warming since the greenhouse effect impacts different regions differently. The earth's average temperature is rising. However, some areas experience more droughts, fires, and heatwaves, while others experience more floods, hurricanes, and winter storms. Not every part of the world is becoming warmer because of greenhouse gases, but we see more extreme climatic events throughout the globe.

The rising global temperature causes the ice sheets near the poles to melt, which raises sea levels. It also leads to more floods, droughts, fires, hurricanes, and the spread of invasive species. Furthermore, money from selling petroleum supports rogue nations like Iran, Russia, and Venezuela. Some profits from crude oil also support terrorist groups such as the Islamic State and Hezbollah.

Fossil fuels have played a crucial role in human history. They fueled the industrial revolution, generated most of our electricity, and powered most of our vehicles. However, they also inflict immense environmental, political, and economic harm. Fortunately, there is an alternative to using fossil fuels. Thanks to the emergence of electric vehicles (EVs) and the falling costs of renewable energy, countries like the United States can switch to an economy with few fossil fuels in a couple of decades. By the middle of this century, most vehicles in the USA, Europe, and East Asia could run on electricity from sustainable sources like solar, wind, and nuclear power.

Switching from a fossil fuels economy to a sustainable energy economy will stabilize the climate, decrease our dependence on energy imports, and create domestic jobs. In a fossil fuels economy, fossil fuels power most transportation and electricity. In a sustainable energy economy, electricity from sustainable resources like solar, wind, and nuclear power transportation.

Humanity is at a crossroads. We must choose whether to rely on sustainable energy or fossil fuels. Choosing to produce our energy from sustainable sources will lead to environmental stability, political independence, and strong economic growth. While we cannot completely stop using fossil fuels, we can make them a small part of our energy profile. On the other hand, if we continue to rely on coal and natural gas to generate most of our electricity and gasoline to power our vehicles, we will experience further environmental degradation, climatic instability, political conflicts, and economic instability.

Shifting to sustainable energy requires a lot of work. It requires sizable public investments in renewable energy, energy storage facilities, smart grids, and charging stations. It will also necessitate political will. Gasoline companies and oil exporters such as Saudi Arabia spend millions of dollars lobbying governments for favorable regulations, subsidies for fossil fuels, and low taxes on gasoline. For decades, the gasoline lobby used a disinformation campaign to encourage voters to support fossil fuels and trivialize concerns about climatic instability. Disinformation refers to incorrect information used to influence people into believing something untrue. We need to combat this campaign with education.

This book describes the challenges of shifting to sustainable energy and how we can overcome them. The first section envisions what an electric future could look like and explains why we failed to switch to EVs in the past. The second section describes the environmental, political, and economic harms caused by fossil fuels. The third section discusses ways to generate and store sustainable energy. Finally, the fourth section details how to combat the oil lobby and what we need to do to create a global partnership for sustainability. We must decide now whether our future will be powered by harmful fossil fuels or will be electric.

PART I: AN ELECTRIC FUTURE

Image by PIRO4D found on https://pixabay.com

CHAPTER 1: IN AN ELECTRIC WORLD

My interest is in the future because I am going to spend the rest
of my life there. Charles Kettering

In the movie *Back to the Future II*, Doc Brown arrives in 1989 with a
time-traveling car to pick up Marty McFly and his girlfriend and fly
them to the future – 2015, to be precise. The movie made several
correct predictions about 2015. It predicted the advent of flat-screen
televisions, smart glasses, 3D films, and, perhaps its boldest
prediction, the Chicago Cubs winning the World Series. While the
Cubs did not win the World Series in 2015, they came close. In 2015,
they reached the National League Championship, and the following
year they won the World Series, ending a 108-year World Series
championship drought.

One prediction that the movie got wrong was flying cars that
turned trash into fuel. We have built flying cars such as the slick-
looking AeroMobil, but they remain a luxury toy for eccentric
billionaires rather than a common form of transportation. Even
though we created various sustainable fuels, over 90% of vehicles in
the USA still use petroleum-based gasoline or diesel fuel. However,
things can change rapidly. We may not see flying cars soon, but we
could live in a world where most cars run on electricity from
sustainable energy within a few decades. This chapter envisions our
lives in a post-petroleum world where vehicles run on electricity from
sustainable sources.

An Electric Future

Imagine living in a world where vehicles run on electricity and
electricity comes from sustainable energy. In this electric world, we
will no longer use gas vehicles that produce dangerous pollutants
such as nitrogen dioxide, carbon monoxide, hydrocarbons, benzene,
and formaldehyde. With no gasoline vehicles or vehicles with other
types of internal-combustion engines, the air will be cleaner and
people healthier. In this world, people living near a highway or busy

streets will no longer need to contend with highway noise. They will watch cars quietly zoom by. Noise from gasoline engines can cause stress and sleep deprivation. By contrast, EVs are quiet.

Commuting to work will no longer require stopping for gas. Gas stations will gradually disappear in this electric world. Instead, most people will charge their cars at work or every evening at home. Most employees will have the option to park their cars next to a charging station and charge their batteries while they work. Shopping malls, supermarkets, schools, and government buildings will likely allow drivers to charge their EVs for free or for a small fee.

Long-distance trips will look different in this electric future. Drivers will no longer need to stop at gas stations along the way. With the range of EVs continuously increasing, most drivers will only need to charge their batteries when they stop to rest each evening. Drivers on multiday trips will charge their vehicles at the hotel parking lots each night. The next day they will be ready to travel once more. Hotels could provide charging at no cost or add it to the room bill.

Restaurants along highways could build charging stations in their parking lots and allow patrons to charge their cars while dining. While drivers might not fully charge their car batteries at restaurants, it will not take long for them to charge their batteries to 80% of their capacity. Presently, fast-charging stations can charge EV batteries to 80% in around half an hour, and in the future, they will do so faster.

In the electric future, businesses will install charging stations in their lots. Drivers will not need to wait by their vehicles to shut off the pumps. Instead, they could head to a convenience store or get something to eat while their cars are safely charging. Drivers will use their mobile devices to receive notifications when their vehicle is fully charged and pay for the electricity. Charging stations will become a way for hotels, restaurants, and retailers to attract clients and generate additional revenue.

Unlike gasoline, electricity is cheap and reliable. Currently, the average cost of charging a Tesla car at home, between $25 and

$33 per charge, is much lower than the price of filling up a gasoline tank. As technology improves and the cost of renewable energy falls, charging an EV will become even cheaper. The price of electricity is far more stable than the price of gasoline. From 2008 to 2011, electricity in the USA fluctuated from $9.74 to $10.60 per kilowatt-hour. During that same period, gas prices seesawed wildly from $4.11 to $1.75 and then back to $3.96 per gallon.

With electricity, families and companies could better plan their transportation expenses. Uber and Lyft drivers will no longer have to fret about rising fuel prices. While there will be differences in the cost of electricity across states, competition and technological advances will make electricity cheap everywhere. American households spend 2% to 6% of their incomes on gasoline. Using EVs will free up disposable income for families.

In an electric world, all public transportation will operate on electricity. Electric trams, subways, and pods will ferry people quietly and efficiently throughout cities. Residents will pay per ride using their mobile device or biometrics. Inside near-vacuum pipes, speedy Hyperloop trains will connect major cities. A five-hour trip from New York to DC through heavy interstate traffic will become a comfortable 20-minute train ride. The Boring Company, founded by Elon Musk, is already building hyperloop trains.

The Path to a Sustainable Planet

Electrifying our transportation is insufficient for achieving environmental sustainability. We must also generate electricity from clean, sustainable resources. If we do not, we could be driving pollution-free EVs, but the additional electricity to charge them would create pollution. We must stop producing electricity from coal and natural gas and rely on sustainable energy instead. As explained in the next section, fossil fuels degrade the environment, create climatic instability, lead to conflicts, and cause economic instability.

Our priority is to eliminate the use of coal, the dirtiest fossil fuel. Burning coal emits greenhouse gases and harmful pollutants such as sulfur dioxide, nitrogen oxide, mercury, and ash. As described in Chapter 4, extracting coal harms the environment and endangers workers. Without coal, the air would be cleaner, especially in developing countries like China and India that use it extensively. Abandoning coal also means eliminating the environmental degradation and fatalities from its extraction. To eliminate the use of coal, we must generate more electricity from solar and wind power. We should also build more nuclear power plants to replace coal power plants. While there are concerns about nuclear power, it is a safe and clean energy source, as discussed in Chapter 11.

After eliminating coal, humanity should eliminate its consumption of natural gas. While natural gas is cleaner and more efficient than coal, it still emits greenhouse gases. Moreover, as discussed in Chapter 6, its extraction through fracking causes water pollution, air pollution, and even earthquakes. Once we eliminate coal and natural gas, our emission of greenhouse gases will significantly fall. To eliminate the use of natural gas, we must expand our renewable energy capacity and build energy storage facilities, as described in Chapter 8.

Petroleum is the most challenging fossil fuel to abandon. As explained in Chapter 5, petroleum harms the environment, leads to political conflicts, and creates economic instability. We could substantially reduce our use of petroleum by switching from gasoline cars to EVs. However, we must continue using petroleum to produce jet fuel, plastics, and other petrochemicals like asphalt for some time. Eventually, we will replace petrochemicals with organic materials from corn or other plants.

Scientists are developing plastics from corn and cotton. However, they are currently difficult and expensive to produce. Chemists want to replace jet fuel with synthesized Iso-Prafins (SIP) from sugars. Material engineers are also paving the way for bioasphalt. For instance, a group of researchers at North Carolina A & T State University developed a bioasphalt from pig manure. This bioasphalt is not only environmentally friendly and cost-effective, but it also helps solve the problem of what to do with animal manure. This bioasphalt is, surprisingly, odor-free. However, it is still unclear if we could use SIP and bioasphalt globally.

According to the Environmental Protection Agency, 65% of all greenhouse emissions come from using fossil fuels and other industrial processes. Eliminating fossil fuels will help stabilize our climate, but it will not be sufficient. We will also need to figure out ways to absorb the excess carbon dioxide in the air. After all, humans have pumped excess carbon dioxide and other greenhouse gases into the atmosphere since the dawn of the industrial revolution.

To combat climatic instability, we must stop cutting down forests and begin replanting trees. Humans have destroyed forests at an alarming rate. Since 1990, we have decimated over one billion acres of forest worldwide. We razed over 17% of the Amazonian rainforest. Forests are essential for climatic stability since they convert carbon dioxide into energy and oxygen through photosynthesis. Trees help eliminate greenhouse gases. We must restore our forests and plant new ones.

In our electric world, power companies will generate electricity from renewable resources. A renewable resource naturally regenerates in a relatively short time. Unlike fossil fuels, renewable energy has little impact on the environment, is everlasting, and does not depend on imports. Much of our electricity should come from solar energy. As illustrated in Chapter 8, solar energy is the cheapest and most abundant energy. Countries will also create renewable energy from wind, hydroelectricity, geothermal plants, waves, tides, and biofuels. Chapter 9 discusses these resources.

Each region will generate electricity based on its natural endowment. The Northwest of the USA will generate electricity predominantly from offshore wind, hydroelectricity, and wave energy. The Southwest will depend on solar panels, concentrated solar power, and geothermal energy. States along the wind corridor from Texas to North Dakota will produce much of their energy from land-based wind turbines. The Midwest will utilize hydroelectricity, biofuels, and offshore wind from the Great Lakes. The Southeast will generate electricity from solar panels, biofuels, and dams. Finally, the Northeast could utilize offshore wind energy and convert trash from its cities into energy.

In an electric future, countries will use computerized electric grids that allow for two-way communication between utility companies and consumers. Households and businesses will store electricity in batteries during low-usage hours and use it during peak usage hours when the cost of electricity from the grid rises. Homes and offices that generate excess electricity from solar panels will sell it back to the grid. During summer and winter breaks, school buildings could become net generators of electricity, which could provide additional revenue for education.

The shift away from fossil fuels will also lead to economic stability. The price of petroleum and natural gas fluctuates wildly due to supply and demand shocks. By contrast, the supplies of renewable and nuclear energies are stable. Moreover, since sustainable energy is local, it creates domestic jobs.

If Not Now, Then When?
The reserves of fossil fuels are finite. Eventually, we will have to stop using them and switch to using sustainable energy. So why do we need to switch from fossil fuels to sustainable energy now? First, if we do not drastically reduce our use of fossil fuels before the middle of the century, our climate will become extremely unstable. Climatic instability is causing costly floods, droughts, hurricanes, and other environmental calamities. These calamities are becoming more frequent and intense. Secondly, the falling cost of renewables has made it possible to switch to a sustainable energy economy. Switching will require a sizable public and private investment in sustainable energy infrastructure. However, we will benefit from lower energy costs, less environmental degradation, and fewer political conflicts.

The earth's average temperature will increase this century due to human emission of greenhouse gases and deforestation. However, the extent of the increase depends on our actions. The

13

Intergovernmental Panel on Climate Change (IPCC) estimates that the earth's average temperature will increase between 2.5 to 10 degrees Fahrenheit over the next century.

The difference between 2.5 and 10 degrees is profound. Higher temperatures cause the ice sheets near the poles to melt and ocean water to expand. The IPCC estimates sea levels could rise between 1 and 10 feet, depending on how far average temperatures increase. A rise of a foot will cause some beach erosion. If the ocean rose by ten feet, it could drown parts of coastal cities like Miami, New York, Bangkok, Jakarta, and Venice. Island nations like Vanuatu and the Maldives could disappear underwater. A sharp rise in temperatures will cause massive droughts in arid regions, large-scale floods, and a fall in global food production. The more quickly we shed our dependence on fossil fuels, the less extreme the change in the climate.

The other reason we should switch to sustainable energy quickly is that it makes economic sense. Until the 2010s, the cost of producing electricity from renewable energy was substantially higher than using fossil fuels. Thanks to technological advancements, producing electricity from solar power costs less than generating it from coal, petroleum, or natural gas.

A study by investment firm Lazard shows that the cost of producing one megawatt per hour of electricity from solar panels decreased from $359 in 2010 to $45 by 2017. By comparison, the cost of producing electricity from natural gas, the primary source of electricity in the USA, decreased from $83 to $60. The cost of electricity from coal fell from $111 to $102 per megawatt /hour. Electricity from wind power is about as expensive as natural gas, but the cost of wind power is also rapidly decreasing.

Other technological improvements make it easier to switch from gasoline cars to EVs. In the past, EVs had a limited range, making them unattractive to most consumers. However, thanks to better batteries, modern EVs can drive for hundreds of miles on one charge. The Tesla Model 3, for instance, can ride for 353 miles, and the Tesla S long-range can ride for up to 405 miles on a single charge. Lucid, a Californian EV manufacturer, developed a car that drives 500 miles without charging. Aptera is developing a vehicle that can ride for a thousand miles on a single charge and charge its batteries using solar panels. EV drivers can now take their cars on long-distance trips as long as they plug them in at night.

Historically, EVs were more expensive than gasoline cars, but this is also changing. In 2021, the cheapest EV available in the USA retailed for around $30,000. However, an article in Business Insider predicts that Americans could soon buy an EV for under $5,000 and perhaps as low as $3,000. This prediction may seem far-fetched, but GM is already selling small EVs for $4,500 in China. Citroën, a French automaker, sells a small EV called Ami for around $6,500 in Europe. EVs have fewer car parts than gasoline cars and require less maintenance since their engines do not heat up. If we continue to invest in building better batteries, EVs will become cheaper, on average, than gasoline cars.

Counter Currents

Switching from a fossil fuel economy to a sustainable energy economy is not a simple task. It is the most monumental change humanity has ever undertaken. However, we must make this change now. There are several objections to investing in sustainable energy and eliminating fossil fuels, but they are mostly unfounded.

Objection 1: Scientists cannot agree whether climatic instability exists or if humans are causing it, so why should we worry about it?

Almost all scientists agree that climatic instability exists. They also agree that we are causing most of it. However, some people are skeptical about it due to a disinformation campaign by the gas industry. This disinformation campaign, discussed in Chapter 12, is designed to create doubt about climatic instability and fear about abandoning fossil fuels. Additionally, if we accepted our role in emitting greenhouse gases and understood their impact on the climate, we would be obligated to switch to sustainable energy. Former Vice President Al Gore called it an inconvenient truth.

Recognizing our role in climate change obliges us to make drastic changes. Therefore, it is easier for some people to ignore or trivialize the problem instead of accepting it.

Objection 2: Why should the USA and Europe invest money in climate control when emitters like China and India are unwilling to cut their emissions?

China, the USA, and India are the world's largest emitters of greenhouse gases. China emits more than twice as much carbon dioxide as the United States, and India belches almost half as much as the USA. China and India, however, have a much larger population than the USA. They have around 1.4 billion inhabitants, more than four times the population of the USA. Their emissions per person are, in fact, significantly smaller than the USA. In 2016, the USA emitted around 15.5 tons, China emitted 7.4 tons, and India emitted merely 1.9 tons of carbon dioxide per person. Both China and India are committed to reducing greenhouse emissions. They both agreed to accomplish carbon neutrality within four to five decades. Carbon neutrality means that the amount of carbon dioxide a country emits does not exceed the amount that nature or technology removes from the atmosphere. Both China and India are investing heavily in renewable energy. China is the world's largest producer of wind power, solar power, and hydroelectricity.

Objection 3: If climatic instability were a concern, national governments would address it.

Democracies have many merits, but one of their shortcomings is that democratic governments often focus on popular short-term objectives instead of unpopular but pivotal long-term goals. Consider the USA's burgeoning national debt, which is over $30 trillion. It exceeds its national income. To control the debt, the government must increase taxes or reduce spending. However, these actions could cause the ruling party to lose the next election. That is why most administrations keep rolling the debt. They prefer to let the next generation deal with it rather than lose an election.

The same thing is true about climatic instability. To curtail greenhouse emissions, governments must take actions that are unpopular in the short run but beneficial in the long run. These actions include increasing spending on renewable energy, eliminating subsidies for fossil fuels, taxing gasoline, and closing fossil fuel power plants, causing some workers will lose their jobs. Consequently, many leaders who understand the importance of addressing climatic instability are unwilling to take the steps needed to address it. Voters must educate themselves and pressure elected officials to make wise decisions.

Objection 4: If solar energy is cheaper than fossil fuels, power and gas companies will generate electricity from solar power. Therefore, there is no need for the government to intervene.

This argument seems sensible. Power companies appear to have an economic incentive to produce electricity from renewable energy instead of fossil fuels. Unfortunately, this argument is incorrect. First, power companies that specialize in generating electricity from coal and natural gas may not have the expertise to generate electricity from renewable energy.

Secondly, although the cost of solar energy is lower per megawatt-hour than fossil fuels, this cost includes the initial capital investment. Power and gas companies own capital for fossil fuels. They built plants, invested in fuel transport like pipelines and ships, and connected their plants to the grid. Therefore, it costs them less to deliver additional electricity using coal and natural gas, which they currently utilize, than to develop the infrastructure needed to generate it from renewable energy.

Thirdly, generating electricity from solar or wind power necessitates a lot of land. Power companies are not large landowners and must negotiate with owners to install wind turbines and solar panels. Wind turbines and solar panels have many parts made of various materials. Therefore, companies would have to rearrange their supply chains to deliver electricity from renewable energy.

17

Lastly, gas companies cannot control renewable energy as they manage their fuel reserves. They cannot own the wind or sunlight. Shifting to renewable energy will liberalize the energy market and cause companies like ExxonMobil and Chevron to lose market power. Therefore, gas companies usually oppose the shift to renewable energy.

Objection 5: Even if current power companies do not shift to renewable energy, new companies have an economic incentive to develop renewable energy and build EVs. Therefore, there is no need for government intervention.
Companies like Tesla, SAIC Motor, and Volkswagen already manufacture millions of EVs. Most other automakers also committed to manufacturing more EVs this decade. Producers such as JinkoSolar, Canadian Solar, and First Solar make billions of dollars from producing and installing solar panels. Other companies are building wind turbines, constructing geothermal plants, and installing underwater turbines. Why do we need the government to intervene if the private market is developing sustainable energy?

Sustainable energy will not succeed without a sizable public investment. To switch to electric transportation, we need to install around half a million fast-charging stations in the USA and millions more around the globe. In 2021, the US had about 5,000 fast-charging stations compared to 136,400 gas stations with multiple gas pumps. Most consumers would not purchase EVs as their primary vehicles unless they could charge them anywhere they traveled. We need large-scale public investment in EV infrastructure.

Similarly, generating electricity from renewable requires expanding our electric grid to regions with abundant wind, sunlight, or waves. Renewable energy manufacturers will not install wind turbines or solar panels in locations far from a grid. We need to expand and modernize to allow sunny states like Arizona and New Mexico to sell excess solar energy to cloudy states like Washington.

We need to support and subsidize sustainable energy. Subsidies will encourage the production of more renewables and cause their costs to fall quicker. Manufacturers learn by doing, so the more renewable energy we manufacture, the less it will cost. Annually, fossil fuels receive over $400 billion in government subsidies. Given the sizable public investment governments make in harmful fuels, is it not reasonable to expect that they invest in sustainable energy?

Objection 6: If we switch to EVs, we will not be able to drive during blackouts. We should stick to gasoline to be on the safe side.

We should think about blackouts and address this concern. We cannot switch to EVs without modernizing our power grid and building energy storage facilities. A smart grid will allow us to shift electricity from different sources, so even if a power plant shuts down or an electricity line collapses, we would still be able to redirect electricity to the area. Additionally, we should store energy locally using batteries, flywheel stations, and sustainable fuel and use it during emergencies. Chapter 10 describes how we can store and redirect energy.

Objection 7: If there is apocalypse, we would be better off with fossil fuels than sustainable energy.

Zombie jokes aside, humanity would be better equipped to handle a global disaster like nuclear war with sustainable energy instead of fossil fuel. During a large-scale disaster, our supply chain for fossil fuels is likely to collapse. Drilling sites, refineries, pipelines, and ships would likely stop operating. Gasoline at gas stations would also have limited usefulness. For starters, we would need electricity to pump the gasoline. Even if we could access the gas, it would work for a couple of years before deteriorating.

By contrast, sustainable energy like solar and wind power are local and long-lasting. Wind turbines and solar panels will continue to operate even after our economy collapses. Furthermore, a sustainable economy will have energy stored in hydro storage facilities, compressed air tanks, and sustainable fuel. When the zombies knock on your door, you will be glad you have a solar panel and an EV that can continue to drive.

If we had Doc Brown's time-traveling car, we could travel to 2050 and see a world where people no longer use fossil fuels. We are unlikely to see a future in which cars run on trash, like in *Back to the Future.* However, if we invest in renewable energy and EV infrastructure now, we can see a future where cars run on electricity in a world powered by sustainable energy.

Objection 8: Does relying on electricity make us more vulnerable to hackers and AI takeover?

Empowering our economy with electricity connected through a smart grid can make us more vulnerable to cyberattacks. After all, most of our homes, vehicles, and factories will rely on the same grid. Therefore, we must be smart about how we build our smart grid. For instance, we must keep the communications, control, and cybersecurity systems separated from the system that controls the grid. We can also install an intrusion detection system to detect and halt potential cyberattacks.

Anyone with access to the grid should receive cybersecurity training. Furthermore, we should retain the ability to separate regions from the grid and temporarily use local energy storage to isolate cyberattacks. Finally, while we should empower most of our vehicles with electricity, it may be wise to use emergency and service vehicles that can work on a secondary fuel like liquid hydrogen. By taking steps to protect the grid, we can build a less vulnerable network than our current, complex fossil fuels infrastructure. According to their website, the US Department of Energy is developing various tools to protect our grid from cyberattacks.

CHAPTER 2: THE PAST WAS ELECTRIC

We are not makers of history. We are made by history.
Martin Luther King, Jr.

In the late 19th century, most people traveled by horse-drawn carriages. By the 1880s, New York City had over 150,000 horses, which its residents used to transport people and freight. At a rate of 22 pounds per horse per day, equine manure added up to millions of pounds each day and over 100,000 tons a year. When a horse died, its body was left in the street until it disintegrated into pieces small enough to pick up. There are pictures from this era of children playing near rotting horse carcasses. Other cities also struggled. In London, the situation was so bad that an 1894 article in The Times wrote, "In 50 years, every street in London will be buried under nine feet of manure."

Not far from New York, Pedro Salom, a chemist, and Henry Morris, an inventor, were working on an alternative to using horses. They equipped a carriage with a motor and a 1,600-pound battery. On August 31, 1894, they took their Electrobat on a ride through the streets of Philadelphia. Their invention caught the eye of William C. Whitney, a New York financier, who helped bankroll the creation of the electric vehicle company, the world's first self-powered taxi company.

At the dawn of the twentieth century, EVs ferried passengers in New York, Philadelphia, and Boston. Unlike horses, electric cars did not leave dung everywhere. They were also quieter, cleaner, and easier to operate than gasoline-powered and steam-engine cars that also started to appear on US streets. It seemed like EVs would become America's vehicle of choice. However, by the middle of the 20th century, they were gone. Almost all the cars sold in the US during the second half of the twentieth century had gasoline engines. This chapter explains why EVs lost the race for dominance and what we can learn from the past to make our future electric.

Losing Steam

At the beginning of the twentieth century, the streets of most American cities were chaotic. US cities constructed roads from brick, stone, or dirt. These roads often had holes, puddles, and humps. Most streets lacked sidewalks. Pedestrians shared the road with horse-drawn carriages, trams, bicycles, and motorized vehicles. Cars had one of three engines, steam, gasoline, or electric, which competed for customers' dollars. EVs led the race, and gasoline cars were a distant third.

By 1912, the production of electric cars in the USA peaked. At that time, around 40% of vehicles in the US used a steam engine, 38% used electricity, and 22% had a gasoline engine. While gasoline cars were the least popular, their popularity rose quickly. By 1925, the world stopped producing steam-engine cars, and electric cars became a luxury for the wealthy. Middle-class Americans chose gasoline cars. How did steam and EVs lose the race to gasoline cars?

The steam engine is the oldest of the three technologies. Thomas Savery invented the steam engine in 1698 to draw water from flooded mines. Steam engines use external combustion, which means that the fluid that powers the engine, like water, is heated by an external source through the engine walls or a heat exchanger. Early steam engines used coal.

In 1801, Richard Trevithick created the first-known steamed-propelled carriage. Trevithick equipped a carriage with a firebox and a boiler in the back. The steam from the engine propelled a piston. His mechanized carriage rode up a hill in Camborne, England, riding nine miles per hour with passengers hanging onto it. Unfortunately, it later caught fire while the driver and passengers celebrated their adventure at a nearby pub. Undeterred, two years later, Trevithick built the London Steam Carriage and rode it on a 10-mile track in London.

The steam engine fueled the industrial revolution by providing power to trains, ships, and machines. However, steam-powered cars remained a scientific curiosity until the end of the nineteenth century. Between 1895 and 1910, multiple US and

European companies built steam-engine vehicles. They used kerosene instead of heavier and less efficient coal. The Stanley Motor Carriage Company, formed by twin brothers Francis and Freelan Stanley, began producing their Stanley Steamer car in 1902. Their car was quite a hit and initially outsold all gasoline-powered cars.

These steam cars had several advantages. People were familiar with the technology and trusted it. They created less pollution than gasoline cars and could drive for longer than EVs. At the beginning of the twentieth century, gasoline was more difficult to find than kerosene. Additionally, many households did not have the electricity to charge an electric vehicle.

However, steam-powered vehicles had several drawbacks. For starters, they were bulky. The once-popular Doble steam car weighed over 5,000 pounds, far more than the electric or gasoline-powered vehicles of the era. It would also take a long time to start the car. It could take half an hour or more to get the engine to heat up, and it might not start on cold days. Despite their early popularity, their drawbacks proved too cumbersome. The production of steam cars began declining in the 1910s, and in 1924 the Stanley brothers sold their last vehicle. While a couple of companies attempted to produce steam-engine cars after 1924, the technology lost its steam. By the late 1920s, two fuels remained in the race—gasoline, and electricity.

Internal Combustion
The internal combustion engine was invented well after steam cars. In an external combustion engine, like a steam engine, the fuel burns in a separate chamber from the engine. The heat warms up water or another fluid causing it to steam. The steam causes the engine's pistons to move. By contrast, in an internal-combustion engine, the fuel is injected into a combustion chamber where compression or an electric spark causes it to explode. The explosion forces the piston up, which causes a crankshaft to move. Consequently, internal-combustion engines are more efficient than external combustion engines, meaning that they convert a higher portion of the energy from the fuel.

23

In 1794, an English inventor named Thomas Mead developed the first gas engine. That same year, Robert Street, a fellow Englishman, patented the first internal-combustion engine to use liquid fuel. In 1807, French engineers Nicéphore and Claude Niépce developed an internal-combustion engine that used controlled dust explosions. However, it took several more decades before anyone successfully used internal combustion to power a car.

In 1876, three German engineers patented the compressed charge, four-cycle engine. Their engine injected fuel into combustion chambers where pistons compressed and ignited it. The pistons connect to a crankshaft that continuously rotates. This process repeats multiple times each minute. Modern gasoline cars go through the four strokes thousands of times each minute.

It took twelve more years before a German engineer named Karl Benz produced the first-known gasoline-powered vehicle. Benz did not attempt to drive his invention. His wife, however, was eager to test his machine. On August 5, 1888, at the break of dawn, Bertha Benz drove off with her two sons, using the petroleum-engine car her husband had built. Her trip from Mannheim to Pforzheim was roughly 100 kilometers long. She did not tell her husband, Karl, about her plans. To accomplish this feat, she purchased a petroleum-based solvent, Ligroin, at a pharmacy and used it as fuel.

Along her journey, Bertha fixed several mechanical problems, had a blacksmith help mend one of the car's chains, and had a cobbler design the world's first brake linings from leather. When she finally reached Pforzheim shortly after sunset, she telegraphed her husband to inform him about her success. Bertha's venture proved that people could use motorized cars for long-distance trips.

Bertha's trip gave birth to gasoline cars. Although, back then, most drivers considered gasoline cars inferior to steam or electric cars. Early gasoline cars were noisy, created toxic fumes, were hard to handle, were rough to drive, had to be hand-cranked, required constant maintenance, and occasionally caught fire. They blackened the streets with soot and emitted toxic gases like nitrogen oxide and carbon monoxide. Running a gasoline car in a poorly ventilated space could prove fatal.

The driver had to use a hand crank to start the engine, which was physically demanding and dangerous. Drivers had to spin the crank around several times until the engine ran. Occasionally, the engine would kick back and send the crank flying out. Sometimes the crank would continue to spin after the engine started and could cause injuries.

It took decades before gasoline cars became the vehicle of choice. Even after they became the dominant vehicle in the 1930s, they had many drawbacks. For decades, gasoline cars spumed lead, which can cause lead poising, sulfur, which becomes sulfuric acid when mixed with water, and particulates, which cause respiratory and cardiovascular diseases.

The US Clean Air Act in 1970 finally forced automakers to create cleaner gasoline cars by improving their exhaust systems. Many states also began requiring periodic tests to prevent vehicles from emitting too many toxins. While gasoline cars are considerably cleaner now than in their early days, they still release pollutants, create noise, and emit carbon dioxide, a greenhouse gas. So how did gasoline cars win the race against their quieter, cleaner electric cousins?

A Spark of Brilliance

EVs are not a new invention; they predated gasoline cars by a couple of years. In 1884, shortly before Karl Benz created the first combustion-engine vehicle in Germany, Thomas Parker developed the first electric vehicle in England. Parker was a brilliant engineer. Historians sometimes refer to him as the Thomas Edison of England. He improved the steam pump, developed a gas engine, improved the alternator, and built the first electric tramway. His electric car looked like a horseless carriage. Parker advocated that his car was safer than other vehicles and better for the environment. However, despite his car's great potential, it got little attention from the public, which did not consider it a viable alternative to horses.

25

In 1888, Philip W. Pratt built and drove the first American electric vehicle in Boston. Pratt created an oversized tricycle that ran on three battery cells. The three batteries weighed a combined 300 pounds. Six years later, Pedro Salom, a chemist, and Henry Morris, an inventor, created and drove a 4,400 pounds EV that they dubbed the Electrobat. They rode it through the streets of Philadelphia, startling pedestrians and causing quite a spectacle. The Electric Storage Battery Company purchased their invention and used it to open up a cab service in Manhattan with thirteen modified Electrobat cars. It later opened cab companies in Boston and Philadelphia. Salom and Morris wanted to take their vehicles on the open road. The duo advocated for a nationwide, electric-powered transportation system with battery chargers throughout the country. The federal government, however, was not interested in investing in charging stations.

EVs provided a quieter, smoother ride than gasoline or steam cars. Drivers did not need to crank their car — they just flicked a switch to get it started. EVs were also considerably easier to maneuver. They were the vehicle of choice for wealthy owners and women. EVs were quiet, easy to drive, and didn't emit smelly pollutants like other vehicles.

Nonetheless, EVs had several challenges. Their batteries were cumbersome. The early EVs used acid-lead batteries. Each battery weighed between 500 and 1000 pounds and had to be removed from the vehicles every few days for maintenance. Battery cells had to be cleaned and topped off. EV owners charged their cars by plugging them into charging stations. However, at the start of the twentieth century, most houses lacked electricity. Many EV owners took their vehicles to charging stations, where they might wait hours to have their batteries charged or repaired.

Battery technology improved at the start of the twentieth century. Thomas Edison created the Edison Storage Battery Company in 1901 to create a better battery for EVs. His early attempts ended in a series of failures. The acid in the battery often ate through its seams, some of the batteries rapidly lost their capacity, and several of his batteries exploded. However, in 1907 Edison developed the nickel-iron battery, which kept its charge for long, was relatively maintenance-free, and lasted four years. These batteries made EVs more appealing. Additionally, in the 1910s and 1920s, electricity spread throughout the United States, and more car owners were getting charging stations in their homes.

The Anderson Electric Car produced the Detroit Electric starting in 1907. EVs quickly gained popularity. Between 1910 and 1912, the sale of EVs in the US tripled. However, these cars had a significant drawback— their limited range. They could only drive for a few dozen miles before their owner had to charge them, and it took hours to charge them. An eccentric chemist and electrical engineer named Oliver P. Fritchle attempted to solve this problem by building an EV that could travel up to a hundred miles on a single charge. In 1908, he drove his Fritchle Victoria model from Lincoln, Nebraska to New York City to promote his vehicles. Fritchle completed the trip, but it took him 18 days since he had to make long and frequent stops to charge his EV. Consequently, his car gained little traction.

The other major obstacle that EVs faced was their cost. In 1912, a gasoline car sold for around $650, while EVs sold for over $1,750. Gasoline vehicles became the everyman vehicle, while EVs became city cars for well-heeled Americans. EVs may have become the vehicle of choice if scientists could have figured out how to make their batteries cheaper and more powerful.

Gas Wins the Race (For Now)

In the 1910s, steam cars were rapidly losing their popularity. However, it was still unclear which type of vehicle would win the fuel feud, electricity or gasoline. EVs could have been the dominant vehicle in the twentieth century if not for a curious and little-known story involving two of America's most famous figures—Thomas Edison and Henry Ford.

Early in its history, the Ford Motor Company weighed whether to focus on gasoline or electric cars. Ford and Edison were good friends and neighbors in Detroit. Edison, whose company produced nickel-iron batteries, convinced Ford to invest in EVs. In 1914, Ford gave Edison a $1.2 million low-interest loan to develop the Ford-Edison electric car. $1.2 million in 1914 was a fortune. Ford also invested his private funds in the project and agreed to purchase 100,000 batteries from Edison.

The Ford-Edison electric car, however, was discontinued in 1919. Some historians believe that gasoline companies put financial pressure on Ford to abandon EVs in favor of gasoline cars. Others claim that Ford's engineers found that Edison's nickel-iron battery did not operate well in cold weather. The engineers switched the nickel-iron batteries with heavier lead-acid batteries making the car too heavy. When Ford discovered this, he reportedly went ballistic and canceled the project. Had Edison and Ford continued to work on their EV, perhaps they would have developed a cheap, high-capacity battery that could have competed with gasoline cars.

Ford never mass-produced EVs. Instead, he focused on the gasoline-engine Model T, which he invented in 1908 to produce a vehicle that middle-class Americans could afford. Ford famously developed the moving assembly line in which the car moved on a track, and each worker completed a specialized task. The moving assembly line allowed the Ford Motor Company to produce numerous vehicles at a low cost. Throughout the 1920s, the Ford Company improved the Model T, making it safer and easier to drive than previous gasoline cars. By the end of the 1920s, the Model T dominated America's streets.

Several inventions helped gasoline cars gain popularity. In 1896, Milton Reeves developed the world's first double muffler. Reeves improved his exhaust muffler over time, making gasoline cars quieter and cleaner. In 1912, electrical engineer Charles Kettering developed the electric starter. Once his invention was adopted, drivers no longer had to hand-crank gasoline cars. Other innovations helped make gasoline cars faster and more reliable.

A surge in petroleum production lowered the price of gasoline and helped raise the popularity of gas cars. Petroleum production increased from 2 million barrels in 1920 to over 10 million barrels a day by 1970. The rise in the number of gasoline cars, in turn, encouraged further investment in oil exploration. Gas companies developed longer, more powerful drills and exploited deeper oil reservoirs.

Another factor that helped gasoline cars dominate in the USA was the construction of highways. Until 1916, intercity car travel was uncommon. The dirt roads that connected cities in the USA were unfit for cars. However, the Federal Aid Road Act of 1916 funded many intercity roads. By 1926, the US government established the Numbered Highway System. EVs were unsuitable for intercity travel due to the lack of charging stations along highways. Moreover, it took a long time to charge EVs. Once Americans started traveling between cities, it no longer made sense for most drivers to buy an EV. The construction of the freeway system in the 1950s and 1960s further cemented gasoline cars as the vehicle of choice.

The roaring 1920s were a period of transformation in the USA. At the beginning of the decade, pedestrians, trams, and horse-drawn carriages shared the streets with steam, electric, and gasoline cars. By 1929, horses had disappeared, pedestrians used newly paved sidewalks, and gasoline cars dominated the streets. While few Americans missed the pervasive stench of horse manure and rotting corpses that permeated city streets in the nineteenth century, many likely preferred the quiet and clean EVs to the noisy and noxious gasoline cars.

EVs lost the first round, but the battle for road dominance is not over. Could the 2020s also be a decade of transformation for transportation as the 1920s were? We should learn from the past. To ensure that EVs dominate the roads this century, we must invest in battery technology and charging stations to help make EVs the technology of choice.

CHAPTER 3: WHO FRAMED THE EV

It is my belief that nearly any invented quotation, played with
confidence, stands a good chance to deceive.
Mark Twain

Eddie, a private detective in LA, is hired by a producer to investigate
whether the wife of one of his stars, Roger, is having an affair with a
wealthy man named Acme. Eddie goes to Roger and shows him
photos of his wife appearing to flirt with Acme. The next day, Acme
is found dead, and Roger becomes the main suspect.

Judge Doom vows to bring Roger to justice for killing Acme,
the owner of Toontown, where cartoon characters live. However,
after he captures Roger, Doom confesses that he was the one who
killed Acme to demolish Toontown and build a highway over it.
While preparing to kill Roger Rabbit and his wife, Doom, the villain
of the film *Who Framed Rodger Rabbit*, explains his vision for a
freeway.

He envisions a "string of gas stations, inexpensive motels,
restaurants that serve rapidly prepared food, tire salons, automobile
dealerships, and wonderful, wonderful billboards reaching as far as
the eye can see." To make his dream a reality, he purchases and
dismantles Los Angeles' beloved transportation system of red trams.
With no alternative means of transportation, people will have no
choice but to use his freeway.

While Doom is fictional, LA's electric red trams were real.
Some film critics believe that Doom represents General Motors. Last
century, GM purchased and dismantled transportation systems in
LA and twenty-five other cities. This chapter will discuss how
American corporations thwarted the development of electrified
transportation and how automakers are reviving them.

Who Killed the Electric Tram?

During the nineteenth century, world cities gradually developed public transportation. In 1835, New Orleans was the first city to build a passenger tram. Horses pulled the trams over a fixed railway. London was the first metropolis to build a cable car, a train pulled by cables. San Francisco established a system of twenty-three cable-car lines between 1873 and 1890. A giant steam engine pulled the cars using cables up its steep hills. Three of these lines are still operational, although they attract more tourists than residents.

In 1881, Berlin in Germany became the first city to build an electric tram. This streetcar ran over a 2.5-kilometer (about 1.6 miles) track. In 1884, Cleveland constructed the first electric streetcar in the US. It only operated for a year, but other cities quickly followed. Four years later, Richmond, Virginia, built an electric tram system that remained operational until 1949. In 1893, New Orleans started powering its streetcar with electricity instead of horses. Chicago constructed the first electric elevated rail line in 1895, and in 1897, Boston opened the first electric underground street railway line.

By the start of the twentieth century, public transportation was developing at an electrifying pace in the USA and Europe. Paris, Berlin, Milan, and other European metropolises created extensive electric tram systems. In 1903, the Pacific Electric Railway Company built the first electric tram in downtown Los Angeles. The company quickly expanded its services to Orange, San Bernardino, and Riverside counties. Their red trams were immensely popular. By 1914, Southern California had over 1,600 trains connecting the communities around LA, making it the most extensive electric railway system on the planet.

However, the Los Angeles red trams did not last long. In 1919, workers staged a massive protest, demanding higher wages and the right to unionize, which increased the company's operating costs. The Pacific Electric Railway Company also had to contend with the rising popularity of personal automobiles in the 1920s and 1930s. With more cars on the streets of LA, the trams had to slow down and use more electricity. Some of its lines became unprofitable.

31

The city proposed to create elevated railways, like in Chicago, or integrate the railway system with the fledging highway system. None of these plans came to fruition.

Between 1938 and 1950, National City Lines gained financial control over the public transportation systems in LA and twenty-five other US cities such as St. Louis, Baltimore, Oakland, and San Diego. National City Lines was a bus company. NCL was jointly owned by General Motors, Standard Oil of California, Firestone Tires, and Phillips Petroleum Company. These companies had something in common—they all benefited from the sales of gasoline cars.

National City Lines dismantled most of the electric transportation systems under its control. By 1969, it dismantled the last electric tram in Los Angeles. Today, little remains of the famed electric transportation systems that once crisscrossed many US cities. New Orleans, Philadelphia, and Boston preserved some sections of their original electric trams. A handful of municipalities replaced their electric trams with light rail systems. However, these systems are small compared to the extensive electrified transportation of the early twentieth century.

Get on the Bus

Did National City Lines dismantle America's electric public transportation to promote the consumption of private vehicles and gasoline? Not necessarily. There were socioeconomic factors that may have led the company to dismantle tramlines. The mass production of cars made them affordable for middle-class Americans. The US also discovered new petroleum reserves in the first half of the twentieth century, especially in Texas and California. As a result, the price of gasoline fell, making driving more affordable. As cities around the US spread outwards, it became cheaper to build roads with bus stops than construct railways. Furthermore, the proliferation of cars made it more difficult for trams to travel on the street and slowed their operation.

We will probably never know whether National City Lines dismantled electric tram lines to promote gasoline cars. Nonetheless, two things are clear. First, the companies that owned NCL, like GM and Standard Oil, had a conflict of interest. They benefited financially from the disappearance of the electric trams since consumers had to purchase more cars, tires, and gasoline. Allowing NCL to acquire public transportation systems is akin to getting a fox to guard chickens.

Secondly, while electric trams did not succeed in the United States, they succeeded elsewhere. Many European cities, including Paris, Vienna, Stockholm, Frankfurt, and Milan, use electrified trams and buses. Vienna, for example, has one of the busiest tram systems. It carries over 363 million passengers per year. Cities outside Europe, such as Melbourne, Kyoto, Hong Kong, and Buenos Aires, also have popular tram systems. Melbourne boasts the largest tram network in the world. Its solar-powered system stretches over 155 miles. If trams succeeded in Europe, Asia, and Australia, why not in the USA?

There may be reasons why public transportation is less successful in the United States. Most Americans live in the suburbs, and it is harder to serve suburbs using public transportation since they sprawl. Furthermore, cars and gasoline are cheaper in the United States than in Europe. In addition, young people in Europe use public transport to get to school. American tourists in Europe are often surprised to see unaccompanied children making their way to school on public buses or trains. Americans use school buses, have their parents drive them to school, or drive if they are sixteen or older.

Besides a handful of cities such as New York, Boston, and Chicago, most Americans rely on their cars for transportation. The USA developed into a car culture. Most Americans use their cars to commute to work, go shopping, travel, and go out. Workplaces, supermarkets, and shopping malls typically provide ample parking spaces. US streets and roads are wide, unlike the streets of many historic cities in Europe and other regions.

It is hard to tell whether electric trams were doomed to fail in the USA. Perhaps if local governments had continued to invest in their electrified transportation systems instead of selling them to a partisan company, USA cities would still be benefiting from electric trams. Perhaps, electric trams will once more serve the streets of US cities in the future alongside EVs.

Don't Call it a Comeback

By the 1960s, Judge Doom's vision had become a reality in the USA. National City Lines had destroyed almost every electric tram, and gasoline cars dominated the nation's roads. The USA built an extensive freeway system that connected all the major cities. As Doom predicted, USA freeways included string gas stations, inexpensive motels, fast-food restaurants, and billboards. Owning a gasoline car became a part of the American dream, and electrified transportation seemed all but dead.

However, something happened in the 1970s that shook the US economy and renewed interest in EVs. In October of 1973, the Organization of Petroleum Exporting Countries decided to cut the supply of petroleum to the US. OPEC is a multinational organization that includes several Arab countries. The organization retaliated against the US for supporting Israel during the Yom Kippur War when Israel had defended itself against an attack by a coalition of Arab nations.

The OPEC embargo profoundly affected the USA. It created a severe shortage of petroleum and caused long lines at gas stations. Many gas stations ran out of gasoline, and gas prices climbed by a staggering 350%. The embargo caused high inflation. Without electric trams and vehicles, Americans had become dependent on gasoline.

The OPEC embargo hurt the US economy and disrupted the lives of Americans. Some people took desperate measures to obtain gas. In Bedford, Massachusetts, a man rented a car from Hertz for a day to siphon the gas from its tank. A builder in Miami purchased a rundown gas station for $10,000 to get its monthly allocation of gasoline for his two Cadillacs. Others took illegal measures such as siphoning gasoline from their neighbors, bribing gas truck drivers, and threatening gas station owners.

The US government was determined not to allow an energy crisis to reoccur. It created the Strategic Petroleum Reserve, which it could use to supply gasoline if OPEC decided to cut supplies again. It also instituted a nationwide speed limit of 55 miles per hour to reduce the demand for gas. In 1975, President Gerald R. Ford imposed Corporate Average Fuel Economy (CAFE) standards that required every auto manufacturer selling cars in the USA to have an average fuel economy for their fleet.

The CAFE standards came into effect in 1978. They initially required car manufacturers to have a fuel economy of eighteen miles per gallon. Automakers could produce less fuel-efficient vehicles as long as, on average, the fuel economy of their fleet met the CAFE requirement. The US Department of transportation gradually raised the required economy.

The high price of gasoline and tightening CAFE standards encouraged some automakers to develop EVs again. General Motors developed a prototype of an electric car. A company called Vanguard-Sebring produced a fleet of EVs called CitiCars. By 1975, it had become the sixth-largest manufacturer in the USA. The US post office purchased 350 CitiCars. However, CitiCars reached a top speed of merely 30 mph and had a range of 40 miles. When the price of gasoline normalized in the mid-1970s, American consumers quickly lost interest in slower, limited-range EVS. In 1977, CitiCars folded. Gasoline prices remained low in the 1980s and 1990s, and Americans' interest in EVs dissipated again.

OPEC learned a valuable lesson from the 1974 oil embargo; if it made gas too scarce, countries would adjust by seeking new technologies. After the 1970s, OPEC focused on making gasoline a profitable but viable fuel. On several occasions, OPEC+, which includes OPEC members plus several other major oil producers, responded to surging demand for gasoline by ramping up the production of crude oil to keep the price of gasoline stable. OPEC+ wants to ensure that we continue using gas for a long time.

Death of a Sedan

Public interest in EVs rose once more in the 1990s. This time, not because of a rise in gasoline prices but because of increasing environmental concerns. In 1990, the California Air Resources Board (CARB) responded to concerns about global warming and air pollution by passing new regulations for automobiles. Air pollution was a big issue in California. Several cities in California, including Los Angles, San Diego, San Francisco, and Bakersfield, suffered from heavy air pollution due to their traffic and climate. Much of California has a Mediterranean climate, and the air tends to stagnate in the summer.

The CARB regulations required automakers that 2% of all vehicles sold in California be zero-emission vehicles by 1998 and 10% be ZEVs by 2003. GM designed a new EV in response. In 1996, it released a sleek and speedy two-door coupe called the EV1. Between 1996 and 2002, GM leased over a thousand EV1s in California and Arizona.

The EV1 received accolades from the media and endorsements from celebrities such as Mel Gibson and Tom Hanks. Hanks was enthusiastic about the EV1 and promoted it on the David Letterman show. A genuine recommendation from Hanks on national television was probably worth more than any advertisement that GM could purchase. However, despite their growing popularity, GM never sold a single EV1, opting instead to retain ownership over its fleet of EVs through a lease program. California subsidized the lease of the EV1 using rebates.

For a moment in history, it looked like GM would lead the EV revolution. In the 1990s, GM was the largest car manufacturer in the world, and it could influence market trends. Other automakers would likely follow suit had GM continued to produce the EVs. If GM had continued to build EVs in the early 2000s, we might have millions more EVs on our roads now. Remarkably, in 2002, General

Motors recalled all its EV1s to the chagrin of many EV1 drivers. The company donated a handful of EV1s to museums and then crushed the rest of them. Despite protests from its clients, GM discontinued the EV1 program in 2003. America's brief flirtation with the electric vehicle was over or at least postponed.

GM never explained why it opted to destroy its EVs, but there were two prevailing theories. The first theory is that GM did not think that EVs were profitable. The California Air Resources Board wanted to force US car manufacturers to sell more ZEVs in California, regardless of profitability. The success of EV1 could encourage California and other states to mandate a higher production of ZEVs. While GM could sell a few thousand electric vehicles to rich celebrities and socialites, it was unclear whether it could sell millions of EVs if states forced it to do so. Perhaps it made sense for GM to destroy the EV1 before the government forced it to produce more.

The second theory is that the oil and gas industry pressured GM to discontinue the EV1. The film *Who Killed the Electric Car* explores this theory. The production of EVs could have benefited the automakers. However, the mass production of EVs would be financially devastating to gas giants such as Chevron and ConocoPhillips. This theory is not unfounded. GM had close connections to gas giants. Even if the EVs were too expensive initially, GM would likely profit from EVs if they continued to build them. Like many manufacturers, the car industry experiences economies of scale, which means the more it produces, the lower the average cost of production. Additionally, manufacturers typically learn by doing, especially with new technologies. Had GM elected to expand the production and sales of its EV1 vehicles, it could learn to produce them at a lower cost.

The EV1 brought GM a lot of positive attention. After all, how many cars get free endorsements from celebrities? GM was battling other American and Japanese car manufacturers that many considered more innovative. Developing a financially successful EV could have helped GM regain its reputation as an innovator and retain its position as an industry leader.

Finally, California and the federal government showed a strong interest in developing more zero-emission vehicles. The states and federal government were probably willing to provide more rebates and tax credits to support their production. Therefore, there are reasons to believe that GM stopped manufacturing the EV1 because gasoline companies pressured it to halt its production.

Who Revived the Electric Car?

Some believe that cats have nine lives. EVs have at least four. EVs lost to gas cars in the 1920s, briefly resurged in the 1970s, and were reborn in the 1990s, only to be destroyed by the company that built them. In 2003, when GM scrapped its EV1 project, Martin Eberhard and Marc Tarpenning formed Tesla. Tesla revived EVs, but can EVs finally become the vehicles of choice?

Tesla needed to raise money to start operating. By 2004, the company had raised $7.5 million, including $6.5 million from Elon Musk, who had received $100 million from selling his interest in PayPal two years earlier. Tesla sold its first car, the Roadster, in 2008. However, its vehicles were unprofitable, and Tesla had to rely on venture capital and government loans to survive. In 2008, Musk became Tesla's CEO, although he continued his involvement with the designs of the cars.

In 2010, Tesla raised $226 million by becoming a publicly-traded company and selling its shares. During the 2010s, Tesla introduced several new models, including the luxury S Model, the Model X SUV in 2015, and its popular Model 3 sedan in 2017. Its sales and market valuations continued to climb. In 2020, Tesla became the most valuable car manufacturer on the planet by market capitalization. Its value skyrocketed even though it sold less than 300,000 vehicles that year compared to over a million cars each sold by Toyota, Volkswagen, Hyundai, Honda, GM, and Ford. By the beginning of 2021, its market value climbed above $800 billion, making it more valuable than the top nine largest manufacturers combined. Tesla's high market capitalization signals that investors expect EVs to become commonplace and Tesla to remain the leader in EV production.

Tesla's meteoric rise stands in contrast to GM's decline. During the twenty-first century, the once-mighty GM lost market share to more innovative and fuel-efficient manufacturers like Toyota, Volkswagen, and Hyundai. When gas prices spiked in 2008, GM lost its place as the largest car manufacturer after seventy-six years on the throne. GM's failure to innovate almost cost its bankruptcy. GM would have collapsed if the government did not give it $50 billion in bailout money.

In 2020, GM was the sixth-largest manufacturer by revenue and market capitalization. What would have happened if GM chose a different part and continued to develop the EV1? In the early 2000s, GM had tremendous funds for developing and marketing EVs. Would GM have been the most valuable automaker instead of Tesla if it had continued to produce EVs?

Tesla revived the EV revolution, but other automakers are catching up. Volkswagen, the largest automaker by sales, is committed to producing 1.5 million EVs by 2025. Toyota, the world's second-largest automaker, plans to develop sixty models of hybrid, electric, and fuel cell vehicles by 2025. Toyota had great success with its hybrid Prius model. Ford is investing $11 billion to develop forty electric models this decade. Jaguar, which produces luxury sports cars, declared it would soon only manufacture EVs. Audi, a German automaker of luxury cars, pledged to exclusively manufacture EVs starting in 2026.

Even GM, which spent much of its history resisting the development of electrified transportation, is planning to produce several electric models, including their monstrous Hummer. The company discontinued the Hummer in 2010 amid criticism over its fuel inefficiency. The Hummer EV will be no less beastly than its predecessor. The top model will have up to 1000 horsepower from its three batteries and tackle a wide range of terrains. Despite its bulky size, GM expects the Hummer EV to leap from zero to sixty mph in

3.0 seconds. More impressively, it will offer an estimated range of 350 miles per charge, allowing car owners to take it on long off-road adventures.

However, Tesla's fiercest competitors might come from China. Chinese firms SAIC and BYD were the second and fourth-largest EV producers in 2021. Nio, a Chinese producer of luxury EVs, gained worldwide recognition and the attention of Wall Street investors. Its market capitalization exceeded $40 billion in 2021. Chinese EV producers have two advantages over other automakers. First, they have unfettered access to the biggest consumer market in the world. Foreign automakers in China have to contend with trade barriers like tariffs. Secondly, the Chinese government subsidizes the production and consumption of EVs.

In 2020, the Chinese bought 4.7 million EVs and hybrid cars, more than any other country. 6.2% of all new vehicles sold in China in 2020 were EVs. By comparison, only 2.3% of new cars in the USA were EVs. Although, 39% of Americans say they would consider purchasing an EV in the future.

European governments also support the production of EVs. Norway, Iceland, Sweden, the Netherlands, Switzerland, Germany, and other countries encourage people to purchase fuel-efficient vehicles using subsidies and investment in EV infrastructure. The Nordic countries lead the charge for switching to EVs. In 2020, 75% of all new cars in Norway, 45% of new vehicles in Iceland, and 32% of new cars in Sweden were electric.

Governments have various policies available to them to encourage people to purchase EVs. They can provide tax credits for EVs, increase gasoline taxes, and invest in research and development for EV technology. However, the most important thing that government should do is to develop EV infrastructure by investing in smart grids and fast-charging stations. With no efficient way of charging their vehicles on the road, most consumers would be reluctant to purchase EVs. Automakers and many consumers want to shift from gasoline cars to EVs, but this shift will not occur without significant public investment.

Even though EVs are increasing in popularity globally, there is no guarantee that they will become the technology of choice. Thrice in the past, EVs gained popularity but failed to become the dominant technology on the road. No one expects a cartoon character to dismantle EVs as Judge Doom dismantled the red streetcars. Nonetheless, some organizations are interested in continuing gasoline production. Furthermore, no matter what commitments automakers make to produce EVs, we need governments to invest in EV infrastructure for them to succeed. We also need governments to build charging stations, tax gasoline, and invest in battery research.

SUMMARY OF PART I

Humanity must stop using fossil fuels and create a sustainable energy economy—an economy with EVs that run on sustainable energy. Switching to sustainable energy will create domestic jobs, reduce political conflicts, decrease pollution, and help stabilize our climate. There were several attempts to popularize EVs in the past, but they failed because EVs were too expensive, had a limited range, and took too long to charge. Furthermore, oil companies and General Motors thwarted the development of electrified transportation in the USA. Currently, there is a strong commitment by Tesla and other automakers to produce EVs. However, EVs will not gain popularity unless governments subsidize them, build charging stations, tax gasoline, and invest in battery research.

PART II: FAULTY FUELS

Image by jplenio found on https://pixabay.com

CHAPTER 4: DISTRESS COAL

We are made wise not by the recollection of our past, but by the responsibility for our future. George Bernard Shaw

On December 5, 1952, a thick fog settled over London. Fogs are commonplace in England, but something was unsettling about this one. Within hours, the sky turned a sickly yellow. Famous landmarks like Big Ben and the Tower of London disappeared in the mist. The air was laden with sulfur and other toxins. It smelled like rotten eggs. A high-pressure cold system settled over the city and prevented its smog from rising. This lethal smog came from burning coal for heating and electricity.

By the middle of the day, visibility was so bad that the government canceled all flights and boat rides. Conductors with flashlights walked in front of London's iconic double-decker buses to guide drivers through the murky streets. Wheezing pedestrians stumbled through the neighborhoods, trying not to slip on the grease-coated sidewalks. Many Londoners developed respiratory illnesses during the Great Smog of 1952, and around 4,000 people died.

Following the crisis, the British Parliament passed the Clean Air Act of 1956, prohibiting burning coal in urban areas. The London Smog illustrates why we must stop using coal. While coal is cheap and abundant, its extraction and consumption are dangerous for people and the environment. Coal contributes to climatic instability and emits toxins such as mercury, arsenic, and carbon monoxide. This chapter discusses the history of coal and how it harms humanity.

Coal Hard Facts

Economists categorize resources as renewable or non-renewable. Renewable resources can regenerate by either reproducing or cycling through nature. They include livestock, plants, water, wind, sunlight, and waves. Non-renewable resources do regenerate—we can only use them once. Minerals, metals, and fossil fuels are non-renewable. Renewable energy comes from renewable resources that are everlasting and usually eco-friendly. Non-renewable energy comes from non-renewable resources like coal, oil, and natural gas. These resources are finite and inflict great harm on the environment.

Before discussing how coal harms our planet, we should understand how coal is created and recognize its importance in history. Coal is a fossil fuel. Fossil fuels are carbon-based materials that form underground from the remains of dead plants and animals. Fossil fuels exist in three forms. Coal is a solid, petroleum is a liquid, and natural gas is, naturally, a gas. Fossil fuels store much chemical energy, which we release by burning them. Humans use fossil fuels to heat their homes, cook, generate electricity, and power machines such as cars.

Most fossil fuels formed during the carboniferous period before dinosaurs roamed the earth. At that time, fern-filled swamps covered much of our planet. Dead ferns sunk to the bottom of these swamps, where the mud buried them. There, the plants deteriorated into organic peat. The muddy, acid swamp water prevented the peat from absorbing oxygen, resulting in slow decomposition. Layer after layer piled over the peat and eventually turned it into fossil fuels under intense heat and pressure. The temperature and the pressure determined if the peat became coal, petroleum, natural gas, or another carbon material such as graphite or diamonds.

Humans have used coals for centuries. Prehistoric humans burned it to generate heat, Romans used it to warm public baths, and Hopi Indians used it to cook and bake pottery. Engineers used it to power steam engines during the industrial revolution. It replaced charcoal as the primary fuel for industrial production. Charcoal is a wood product that is easier to burn than coal but is dirtier and contains less energy.

Today, we mainly use coal to generate electricity. In 2013, 41% of global electricity came from coal, making it the primary source of electricity on the planet. Although, since then, its share has decreased due to the increasing popularity of natural gas and renewable energy. By 2020, only 37% of electricity in the world came from coal.

In the United States, 23% of the electricity comes from burning coal. Natural gas generates over 38% of the electricity in the USA, making it the country's primary energy source. Coal, however, is still the dominant source of electricity in many developing countries. China and India, the two largest developing economies, rely on it to produce electricity because they have large coal reserves and find it easier to handle than natural gas.

Coal accumulates in large underground layers known as seams that can reach hundreds of miles in length. For centuries, traders only extracted coal near the surface. In 1575, Sir George Bruce of Carnock constructed the world's first coal mine. Mining allowed us to extract better quality coal. Generally, coal that is formed deeper underground under higher pressure is purer. Purer coal stores more energy and creates less pollution.

There are different kinds of coal. Lignite coal contains the least energy and has a carbon content of 25% to 35%. It easily crumbles and releases toxins and flammable gases, making it dangerous to transport. Since it is often close to the surface, it is typically extracted using open-pit mines and is converted into energy nearby. Germany, Greece, and Texas use lignite coal to generate electricity.

Sub-bituminous coal is newer than lignite coal. It has a carbon content of 35% to 45% and makes up 45% of the USA coal supply. Bituminous coal contains 45% to 86% carbon and generates most of the electricity from coal. Russia, Colombia, and the Appalachian Mountains of the USA all have it. We also used it to forge metals and light street lamps. Anthracite, the purest form of coal, is rare and is primarily used for stoves and furnaces since it creates little soot.

Deadly Digs

Coal is a widely used energy source, but its extraction comes at a great price. Companies extract the coal using underground or surface mining. Underground mining is dangerous to miners. In the USA, over 105,000 coal miners died from crushing mine walls, toxic gases, electrocution, underground explosions, oxygen deprivation, or mechanical accidents. Fifteen times as many miners were seriously injured.

Historically, companies extracted coal by digging a vertical shaft to explore coal seams. After reaching a seam, the company would burrow horizontal tunnels to access the coal. In the early days of coal explorations, miners dug for coal using pickaxes or other tools. Now, mining companies use a continuous miner machine with a large cutting drum to dig access tunnels. These tunnels are sometimes so long that miners install underground trains to move through them.

Once the company creates and secures a tunnel, the miners use a longwall shearer with a giant wheel of rotating teeth to cut along the wall. A longwall shearer can dig an astonishing 50 tons of coal per minute. Miners then transport the crushed rocks using conveyed belts to a water tank to separate rocks and sediments from the coal. Then, it is dried, placed on a hopper, loaded on trains or trucks, and transported to power plants.

Underground mining is unsafe. Miners work alongside large, rapidly moving excavators, conveyor belts, trains, and other equipment. Mining equipment can be very loud and damage miners' hearing. Tunnel walls can collapse and injure, kill, or trap miners underground. Most tunnels are very deep, making it challenging to rescue trapped miners.

In 2010, thirty-three miners were trapped 2,300 feet underground in a copper-gold mine near Copiapó, Chile. It took seventeen days of drilling exploratory boreholes before the rescue crew found a note taped to the drill bit that stated that all thirty-three miners were alive. However, since the miners were trapped deep underground, it took sixty-nine days before the rescue team could hoist the men to the surface. The incident, depicted in several books and a film starring Antonio Banderas, reminded everyone how dangerous underground mining is.

Miners also risk being exposed to toxic gases. The most dangerous gas is carbon monoxide. CO is a colorless, odorless gas that is often trapped underground. It causes tissue damage or death by replacing the oxygen in the blood. People can pass out and die from CO without ever realizing that they are inhaling a toxic substance. Harmful gases like nitrogen oxides and hydrogen sulfide are also common in mines.

For decades, miners carried canary birds down to mines. Canary birds are sensitive to toxins and become agitated when they detect them. Miners eventually replaced canaries with electronic detectors. These detectors made mining safer, yet exposure to toxins is still commonplace.

Miners must also worry about methane. Methane is a gas that forms during coalification, which is the transformation of peat into coal. It is common in mines. Methane is both toxic and highly flammable. Methane can cause asphyxiation by displacing oxygen. It can also easily ignite by a spark from a machine and is the most common source of underground explosions.

While methane causes most mining explosions, the presence of coal dust can magnify them. Coal dust is a fine powder created when coal is crushed or pulverized. It is explosive and dangerous to breathe. When methane explodes, it creates a pressure wave that can spread and burn coal dust throughout a mine. In the early 1900s, thousands of coal miners perished annually from underground explosions. The worst incident was in 1907, when 362 miners died in Monongah, West Virginia, in an underground explosion. While underground explosions are less common now, they still pose a risk for miners. Between 1986 and 2010, there were ten fatal explosions in underground mines.

Miners can inhale various harmful chemicals. The Centers for Disease Control and Prevention (CDC) lists arsenic, nickel, lead, cadmium, manganese, platinum, cobalt, mercury, cyanide, sulfur dioxide, and xanthates as some of the dangerous chemicals that can harm miners. These chemicals cause various symptoms, such as chemical burns and lung cancer. Miners are also constantly exposed to coal ash, asbestos, and dust that often lead to pneumoconiosis – a respiratory disease caused by scarring of the lungs leading to coughing and shortness of breath. The longest word in the English language, pneumonoultramicroscopicsilicovolcano-koniosis, means a lung disease caused by inhaling ash or dust.

Underground mining is dangerous to workers, but it also harms the environment. Chemicals released by mining can leach into the watershed and taint the local water supply. Methane from mining can cause climatic instability. Methane is the main component of natural gas and is often used to generate energy. Mining companies capture methane from mines and use it as fuel. About 5% of the natural gas produced in the USA comes from mines. However, some methane invariably leaks into the atmosphere and acts as a greenhouse gas. Methane traps twenty-one to twenty-five times more heat than carbon dioxide.

Mining companies have got more efficient at capturing methane and have reduced the number of explosions by installing electronic detectors, improving ventilation, and sealing off inactive parts of mines. Miners also regularly spread limestone powder inside mines. If there is an underground explosion, the limestone powder absorbs most of the heat, which helps stop the blast from spreading. While underground mining in the twenty-first century is safer than in the past, it is still a dangerous profession. The Bureau of Labor Statistics estimates that the fatality rate in the coal mining industry was 24.8 per 100,000 in 2007, which is six times the average rate for workers in the USA.

Scratching the Surface

In recent decades, mining companies shifted to surface mining. Surface mining involves removing soil and rock from the surface to extract the coal underneath. Surface mining has existed since the 16th century, but modern excavation equipment and explosives allow companies to dig deeper and faster. This process is more cost-effective and safer for workers than underground mining, but it is more harmful to the environment. It is also detrimental to the surrounding communities.

There are three methods of surface mining: strip mining, open-pit mining, and mountaintop removal. Strip mining exposes coal near the surface. The soil is removed using explosives and excavators and carried away in giant trucks. Companies typically use large excavators to crush and remove rocks. One of the biggest excavators, the Badger 293, is 315 feet tall and 738 feet long. It weighs an astonishing 14,200 tons (39 million pounds), about the weight of 2,000 elephants. It has eighteen enormous buckets that remove 15 cubic meters (529.7 cubic feet) each second.

Strip mining harms the environment in multiple ways. Mining companies must remove the soil and vegetation above the rock, called the overburden, destroying animal habitat. Excavations create dust and may release toxins. Mining companies keep the excavation sites wet to minimize the dust, but some dust inevitably spreads through the air. Mining equipment creates loud sounds that disrupt animals and are dangerous to employees. One CDC study found that mining equipment generates noise ranging from 80 to 120 decibels. Any noise above 70 decibels is unsafe for people.

Companies use open-pit mining to excavate minerals that are deeper underground. Coal deeper underground is often better quality than coal near the surface. However, the deeper the mining companies dig, the more chemicals they potentially release. Open-pit mining can introduce toxic chemicals such as arsenic and mercury into the watershed and compromise local water reservoirs. Additionally, mining exposes sulfides. When the rainwater dissolves the sulfides, they form acids, harming plants and animals. Open-pit mining damages the environment and forever scars the land.

Open-pit mines can permanently change a region. For example, a mine in Hambach, Germany, covers an area of five by six miles. Creating this mine required clearing large swathes of native forests and relocating several towns. The impact on the surrounding community was profound.

Strip and open-pit mining harm the environment but the most damaging form of mining is mountaintop removal (MTR). Mining companies developed MTR techniques in the 1970s in the Appalachian region of the United States. It involves digging holes into mountains where coal seams are located, blowing them up, and clearing the loose soil with excavators and draglines.

Draglines are colossal machines that weigh between 8,000 and 13,500 tons and have a long crane with a giant metal bucket at the end. Big Muskie, the largest dragline, can excavate 170 cubic meters (220 cubic yards), about the size of two buses, with each scoop. Mining companies usually dump the excavated soil in a nearby valley. The discarded debris often blocks streams and alters the ecosystem.

MTR mining became popular in the 1990s and 2000s when the price of petroleum rose, making coal more competitive. MTR is cost-efficient and relatively safe for workers. It provides jobs in the Appalachian region. It helped revive coal production in the Appalachians after a steady decline from 1950 to 1990.

Sadly, MTR led to the destruction of hundreds of mountains and local streams. The process decimated multiple ecosystems. The mining releases dangerous chemicals such as lead and cadmium. Despite the presence of retention ponds, rain can move these chemicals from open mines to local watersheds. While some mining companies attempt to restore areas once they use them, the restoration is never complete, and the mountain is gone forever.

Coal mining is harmful to workers, local communities, and the environment. Despite safety improvements, underground mining is dangerous to miners. Surface mines are safer for employees but far more harmful to local communities and ecosystems. The extraction of coal comes at a great price.

Bad Coal

Excavating coal killed thousands of miners and strained many ecosystems. Yet, the harm from extracting coal is minor compared to the devastation from burning coal. Burning coal produces carbon dioxide, sulfur dioxide, soot, mercury, and other dangerous byproducts. Our use of coal contributes to climate instability, acid rain, respiratory illnesses, and cancer.

Once burned, the carbon in the coal combines with the oxygen in the air to form carbon dioxide, the most significant greenhouse gas. Greenhouse gases trap some of the heat emitted from the earth's surface. These gases are necessary for our survival. Without them, our planet would be bitterly cold, with an average temperature of 0 degrees Fahrenheit. However, human activity like burning fossil fuels causes greenhouse gases in the atmosphere to increase faster than the earth can absorb them. As a result, the earth's average temperature is rising.

The greenhouse effect is causing various changes. The biggest concern is the ice sheets around the northern and southern poles. Melting ice sheets will cause the earth's sea level to rise by one to eight feet by the end of the twenty-first century. Rising sea levels will cause more floods, damage coastal towns, and drown low-lying island nations like the Maldives, Tuvalu, and the Marshall Islands.

According to the National Aeronautics and Space Administration (NASA), the greenhouse effect is causing various extreme climatic events such as hurricanes, droughts, floods, and species invasion. Hurricanes form when warm, moist ocean air rises and becomes twisted by winds in the upper atmosphere. The rising temperatures of oceans are causing an increase in the number and intensity of hurricanes.

We are also seeing changing precipitation patterns. Some areas like the Southwest of the USA and Mediterranean Europe are experiencing more fires and droughts. By contrast, the Eastern Seaboard in the USA, East China, and Western Europe are experiencing more floods.

In 2021, the Henan Province in China experienced record floods that inundated multiple cities and killed over 300 individuals. That same year, Germany and the Netherlands suffered unprecedented floods that killed over 220 people and destroyed many homes. That same year, the Pacific states in the USA saw a record number of fires while Greece suffered the worst fire in its history.

An analysis of satellite data shows that the likelihood of intense hurricanes with sustained wind of 110 mph or higher has increased by 8% each decade since the 1970s. These tropical storms cause surges that damage beaches, winds that destroy structures, and heavy rains that cause floods. They can devastate entire regions.

Warming oceans also cause corals to bleach. Coral reefs are large colonies of polyps, small vase-shaped animals that secrete calcium. The calcium provides the structure for the reef. The polyps have a symbiotic relationship with algae called zooxanthellae that lives inside their tissue. The polyps shelter the algae and provide it with organic waste. In return, the algae produce oxygen, remove organic waste, and supply energy to the polyps.

Algae have various colors and give reefs their brilliant hues. When the water warms, the zooxanthellae can become toxic, which leads the polyp to expel them. Without the colorful algae, the coral turns white. Corals do not die right away from bleaching, but since the algae provide around 90% of the coral's energy, it becomes vulnerable and often collapses.

Despite the decrease in the use of coal, coal-fired power plants continue to be the single largest emitter of carbon dioxide, accounting for 30% of all its energy-related emissions. The International Energy Agency estimates that coal has caused over 0.3 degrees of the one-degree Celsius increase in earth's temperatures since the late 1800s. Coal is the leading cause of global climatic instability.

Ban-Ki Moon, the former Secretary-General for the United Nations, stated, "Climate change is the single greatest threat to a sustainable future. But, at the same time, addressing the climate challenge presents a golden opportunity to promote prosperity, security, and a brighter future for all." Climate change helps aid the spread of invasive species.

A warming climate is helping the pine beetle spread into colder regions of North America. The pine beetles destroyed millions of hectares in Western Canada and the USA. As the climate warms, tropical species of mosquitoes are migrating poleward and spreading tropical diseases such as yellow fever, dengue, chikungunya, and Zika.

The biggest concern about using coal is its emission of greenhouse gases. Coal also emits other dangerous chemicals such as sulfur, nitrogen, mercury, cadmium, and arsenic. Sulfur and nitrogen combine with water to create acid rain. While acid rain does not harm humans directly, it harms plants and insects, which are the foundations for many ecosystems. Acid rain also damages the exterior of buildings and devalues property.

Burning coal releases toxic chemicals such as mercury, cadmium, and arsenic. Many of the fish we eat absorb mercury. Its consumption can cause birth defects or mercury poisoning, which can cause irritability, muscle weakness, and memory loss. Arsenic, another byproduct of coal, is deadly, and its consumption can cause vomiting, muscle cramps, and even fatalities.

Burning coal also generates particulates, small particles that float in the air. These particles can cause respiratory diseases and are carcinogenic; they increase the probability of cancer. While large-scale pollutions like the one caused by the London Fog of 1952 are no longer common in developed countries, they are still common in developing nations that heavily use coal.

The Clean Coal Controversy

Recently, scientists developed technologies to make coal safer for people and the environment. There are two main methods for achieving this. Companies can crush coal and wash it, often using chemicals, before utilizing it. Alternatively, they scrub byproducts from the smoke stocks after they burn coal.

The energy industry refers to coal treated using these methods as clean coal. In reality, clean coal is hardly clean! While treated coal releases fewer toxins than untreated coal, it still emits climate-altering gases like carbon dioxide and nitrous oxide.

Additionally, the chemicals used to purify it are toxic. Nonetheless, the US government spends billions of dollars on clean coal.

A study of Duke Energy Corp, which received millions of dollars from the government to utilize clean coal technologies, found that its North Carolina plants produced more sulfur dioxide after employing clean coal technologies. While sulfur dioxide is not a greenhouse gas, it combines with carbon to produce aerosols that could cause lung diseases. Moreover, sulfur dioxide bonds with water vapor to create acid rain.

The chemicals used for cleaning coal are toxic. Power companies use bromide to remove mercury from coal. Bromide can bond with chlorine to create a carcinogen called trihalomethanes. The watershed around Charlotte had elevated levels of trihalomethanes after the local coal power plants started treating coal with chemicals. Similarly, in 2012, the South Carolina Department of Health & Environmental Control found elevated levels of trihalomethanes in Lake Moultrie and ordered the local coal power plant to stop using bromide to clean coal.

According to the Energy Information Administration's data, out of fifty-six power plants that received subsidies to utilize clean coal technologies, only eighteen managed to reduce the emission of nitrogen oxide by over 20% as required by the program, and they did so partly by switching away from coal. Nitrogen oxide creates acid rain and contributes to the formation of tropospheric ozone, another greenhouse gas.

Power companies promote their coal as clean, implying that it does not harm the environment. They receive hefty tax credits to utilize largely ineffective technologies that can cause additional harm. The harm from coal is not as visible as the Great Smog of London, which was produced by burning coal and killed over 4,000 people. However, coal is detrimental to people, plants, and the planet. We must eliminate our use of coal within two decades. It provides a cheap way to produce electricity, but it inflicts too much harm.

CHAPTER 5: CRUDE OIL

We cannot remain looking inwards at ourselves on a small and
increasingly polluted and overcrowded planet.
Stephen Hawkins

The fire burned for ten months, consuming an estimated 5 million
barrels of oil a day. It shrouded the entire region in thick, black
smoke. In Damascus, Syria, 800 miles away, the rain was black.
Massive flames shot up from the 700 oil wells that Saddam Hussein,
Iraq's president, had set aflame in a desperate attempt to slow down
the advancing US-led alliance before his army retreated from
Kuwait. John Kelly, the assistant secretary for Near Eastern Affairs,
described the fire as "a scene out of Dante's Inferno." Saddam
unleashed one of the gravest environmental disasters in history.

The burning of Kuwait's oil fields in 1991 demonstrated the
potentially devastating impact of petroleum on the environment.
Throughout history, petroleum has been a blessing and a curse.
Petroleum is a versatile and powerful compound. We use petroleum
to power vehicles, fly airplanes, heat our homes, generate electricity,
create plastics, and produce asphalts. However, its extraction,
transportation, and use generate pernicious pollution, contribute to
climatic instability, lead to political conflicts, and help fund violence.
This chapter explores the benefits and challenges of using petroleum
and explains why we must quickly stop using it.

Black Gold

Petroleum, also known as crude oil, is a mixture of hydrocarbon
compounds found beneath the earth's surface. The hydrocarbon
molecules store chemical energy that is released by burning it. Like
coal, petroleum is a fossil fuel. It formed when dead organisms were
buried underneath sedimentary rock and transformed under intense
heat and pressure.

Petroleum is a versatile liquid. It had many uses throughout
history. It was used over 4,000 years ago in Babylon as tar for

construction. The Chinese and Japanese used it for lighting and heating, starting in the seventh century AD.

In the nineteenth century, kerosene, a petroleum product, replaced whale oil as the primary fuel for lighting in the West. Whaling was grueling, gruesome, and dangerous work. Whaling boats would travel thousands of miles, and whalers would sometimes not see their families for years. Conditions on whaling boats were dismal. Whalers frequently died from diseases, malnutrition, hypothermia, or at the hand of pirates. Until the introduction of the harpoon gun in the late nineteenth century, whalers had to approach whales with rowboats and attack them with harpoons and spears. Many died during these savage hunts.

Whaling was also unsustainable. Whalers slaughtered around 2.9 million whales in the nineteenth century and drove several species to the brink of extinction. For instance, whalers killed more than 90% of all blue whales for their blubber. Kerosene provided a safer, cheaper, and more sustainable way to light our streets, and its use saved several whale species from extinction.

Gasoline is another petroleum product. At first, scientists considered it an undesirable byproduct of kerosene. People did not recognize gasoline as a valuable fuel until 1892, and it only gained popularity in the twentieth century. Gasoline demand started to grow after the Ford Company built the T-model in 1908 and popularized gasoline cars. Less than a decade later, in 1916, gasoline production surpassed kerosene for the first time.

Gasoline cars created a surge in demand for gasoline. The Middle East, Texas, North Dakota, Alaska, California, and other oil-rich regions experienced economic booms. Gasoline stores an incredible amount of chemical energy that can be used to power engines or generate heat. According to the Environmental Protection Agency, the average fuel economy for vehicles in the USA was 25.5 miles per gallon in 2020. A sedan with a typical gasoline tank of 16 gallons can drive for over 400 miles, or the distance between Baltimore and Boston, without stopping to refuel.

We are getting better at converting energy from gasoline. Between 2004 and 2020, for example, US car manufacturers increased the average fuel economy of vehicles by 30% while increasing their horsepower by 14% and reducing their carbon dioxide emissions by 23%. Automakers are making cars aerodynamic, utilizing computers to maximize fuel efficiency and engineering parts with less friction.

We also use petroleum to produce jet fuel. Gasoline consists of hydrocarbons that contain between seven and eleven carbon atoms. Jet fuel contains hydrocarbons with twelve to fifteen carbon atoms. Consequently, jet fuel has more energy and freezes at a lower temperature than gasoline, which is pivotal since planes fly miles above the earth where the air is freezing.

Chemists and material engineers break the hydrocarbon molecules in crude oil to create benzene, butadiene, propylene, and other petrochemicals. These chemicals produce plastics and other materials. Plastics are waterproof and do not conduct electricity. We use them to make bags, textiles, electronic components, containers, toys, and construction materials. Around 9% of petroleum worldwide is used to produce plastics, but demand for plastics is rising. In 2015, the world created over 400 million metric tons of plastic. The COVID-19 pandemic accelerated the need for plastic for packaging and Personal Protective Equipment.

Manufacturers use propylene, another petrochemical, to create acrylics, rubbing alcohol, glue, and carpets. They use butadiene to make synthetic rubber and paper coatings. They use benzene to produce lubricants, dyes, detergents, drugs, and pesticides. Many medications and beauty products also use petrochemicals. Clearly, petroleum supports many human needs.

Destruction by Extraction

If petroleum is a versatile and economically important liquid, why should we stop using it? Because the exploration, extraction, transportation, and use of oil are detrimental to nature and people. The search for petroleum often harms animals. Oil companies typically search for crude oil using seismic blasts that send sound waves underground. They analyze how these waves bounce off different layers below the surface to determine the likelihood of an underground oil reservoir.

Exploratory seismic blasts can be as loud as 250 decibels. A firecracker generates a 150-decibel blast. A 250-decibel sound blast is ten trillion times louder than what the CDC (Center for Disease Control and Prevention) considers harmful to humans. On land, seismic blasts can scare animals and disturb their living patterns. In the ocean, where sound waves carry faster and further, they devastate ecosystems. These blasts can damage marine mammals' hearing, disorient them, disturb their feeding, and disrupt their breeding patterns. A US Department of Interior study found that seismic exploration in the Gulf of Mexico and the Atlantic has killed or injured 138,000 dolphins and whales. Another research discovered that seismic blasts could kill up to 90% of fry or young fish.

Once a company discovers a potential oil reservoir, it begins drilling exploratory wells. Companies often drill multiple wells before they find petroleum. Drilling wells often necessitate clearing swaths of vegetation and bringing heavy, loud equipment to remote and sometimes ecologically vulnerable areas. It destroys animals' habitats and disrupts their lives.

Drilling is also dangerous to workers. According to the CDC, the fatality rate of oil workers is roughly seven times higher than the average for US workers. Rig workers work with heavy, rapidly moving equipment, and mud can make the drill slippery and dangerous. The work is fast-paced, and accidents are common.

Petroleum exists in underground reservoirs, often under high pressure. If the pressure is too high, the oil pushes the drill up, an effect known as a blowout. Blowouts can injure workers and release gases like methane or carbon dioxide. Carbon monoxide is toxic, and methane can ignite and explode.

Blowouts sometimes occur in offshore drilling sites, where they can cause spills. The biggest blowout in history occurred in 2010 in the Gulf of Mexico on the Deepwater Horizon rig. The blowout killed eleven workers and released an estimated 4.9 million barrels of crude oil into the Gulf of Mexico. The massive spill killed countless fish, crustaceans, and marine mammals. It took British Petroleum, which owns the rig, eighty-seven days to stop it and longer to contain it. The massive spill devastated the local fishing industry. Since it took place in the summer, it also hurt tourism around the Gulf Coast.

Oil companies keep digging deeper and deeper below the ocean. In the past, most ocean drilling occurred in shallow water. However, between 2005 and 2015, deep-water exploration increased by 25%. Perdido, the deepest floating rig in the world, is located in the Gulf of Mexico at a depth of 8,040 feet. The Deepwater Horizon rig drilled at a depth of 5,100 feet. Every 33 feet add another atmosphere of pressure. Deeper rigs experience more pressure on the drill and pipes, making it harder to block leaks. If a deep-ocean well like Perdido spills, it will be extremely difficult to contain.

Petroleum and Pollution
The extraction of petroleum is dangerous for workers and ecosystems. The transportation and consumption of petroleum products pose additional risks to people and the environment. Oil companies transport petroleum to refineries that process it into gasoline, diesel fuel, jet fuel, and petrochemicals. Then, the petrol products head to gas stations, factories, and storage tanks. Leaks are commonplace during transportation.

The US transports around 70% of its oil by pipelines, 23% by tankers, 4% by trucks, and 3% by trains. One of the most famous oil spills happened in 1989 with a tanker owned by Exxon called Valdez. The supertanker collided with a reef, spilling 10.8 million gallons of oil into the environmentally rich Prince William Sound off the coast of Alaska. As later discovered, the ship's captain was drunk during the incident. When tested ten hours after the collision, his alcohol level had been ten times the allowable limit. The third mate, whom he placed in charge of the ship, had not been licensed to pilot the vessel.

While the Exxon Valdez spill is one of the most famous, it is hardly unique. In the 1980s, oil tankers caused an annual average of 9.4 spills. Since then, the number of incidents has decreased to 1.8 per year. However, these spills are still damaging. In 2020, a Japanese-owned carrier struck a reef off the southeast coast of the island of Mauritius in East Africa, spilling over 1,000 tons of oil and destroying its pristine reefs.

Oil can also spill from pipelines. In 2019, 9,000 barrels of oil spilled from the Keystone XL pipeline in South Dakota. The pipeline's construction led the Fort Belknap Indian Community of Montana and the Rosebud Sioux Tribe of South Dakota to sue the federal government for violating the US treaty with the tribe. The pipeline placed their water supply and sacred tribal lands at risk.

In another incident, in 2021, the government charged Amplify Energy and its subsidiaries with negligence for allowing 25,000 gallons of oil to spill off the coast of Southern California. Investigators believed a cargo ship had weakened the pipeline when it dragged its anchor over it. Amplify Energy never fixed or reported the problem.

Since oil is flammable, trains and trucks carrying oil can explode. In 2013, a train carrying seventy-two oil tanks in Quebec, Canada, derailed and exploded. The incident leveled thirty buildings and killed forty-seven people. More recently, a truck carrying fuel exploded in Haiti's second-largest city, damaging over thirty houses and killing at least seventy individuals. Transporting oil is dangerous to people and nature!

While oil spills are concerning, the biggest concern with petroleum is that, as with coal, burning it releases greenhouse gases. According to the Environmental Protection Agency, a typical gasoline-powered car emits about 4.6 metric tons of carbon dioxide annually. Gas cars produce two other greenhouse gases, methane, and nitrous oxide. As noted earlier, greenhouse gases trap heat in the earth's atmosphere, leading to climatic instability. Consequently, our planet experiences more hurricanes, floods, fires, and droughts.

In the past, coal was the main culprit for climatic instability. However, due to the rising global demand for cars and the falling use of coal, petroleum is now the largest source of anthropogenic greenhouse gases. 46% of greenhouse gases from fossil fuels come from oil, 33% from natural gas, and 21% from coal.

The rising demand for gasoline cars is increasing our consumption of gasoline. Between 2005 and 2015, the number of vehicles around the globe increased from 892 million to 1.28 billion. In the USA, the number of vehicles rose from 238 million to 264 million during this period.

The rise in car ownership in the West pales in comparison to the surge in car sales in Asia, which is fueled by rising income and cheaper, domestic cars. Vehicles sold in China rose from a mere 91 million in 2010 to 281 million in 2020. In 2019, India added over 51,000 vehicles a day to its already congested roads. As humanity consumes more gasoline, it emits more greenhouse gases.

Greenhouse gases are not the only pollutants that gasoline generates. Burning gasoline also releases carbon monoxide, a colorless, odorless gas that can cause dizziness, headaches, shortness of breath, blurred vision, confusion, and even death. In the past, people could commit suicide by running their cars inside closed spaces and inhaling carbon monoxide. Modern vehicles have catalytic converters that convert carbon monoxide to carbon dioxide. Nonetheless, even modern gas cars emit some carbon monoxide.

Poorly maintained gasoline engines also emit particulates. When inhaled regularly, these particles can cause respiratory diseases like asthma and cardiovascular disease. Petroleum is a versatile liquid, but it harms people and nature in multiple ways. We must phase out our use of petroleum products.

Petroleum Politics

The harm that petroleum inflicts is not limited to the environment. Our dependence on crude oil has led to wars, civil conflicts, terrorism, and economic instability. Groups and countries have fought to control the earth's dwindling petroleum reserves, and some of these conflicts have led to supply shocks that have disrupted economies.

The first-known war over petroleum was the Chaco War between 1932 and 1935. Bolivia and Paraguay fought over control of the northern part of the Gran Chaco region, a semiarid lowland region divided between Bolivia, Paraguay, and Argentina. Before the twentieth century, the area was sparsely populated and of little economic importance. The discovery of oil reserves in the region led the two nations to fight over it. Many died during this conflict.

Wars over oil occurred in other regions too. Between 1980 and 1988, Iraq and Iran engaged in a prolonged military conflict. While there were several reasons for the war, including tensions between the Shia-dominated leadership of Iran and the Sunni-dominated leadership of Iraq, oil played a pivotal role. Specifically, Iraq supported separatists in the oil-rich Iranian territory of Khuzestan. The separatists sought to create a new Arab state known as Arabistan. Naturally, Iran was unwilling to lose this economically valuable territory.

In 1990, shortly after the Iran-Iraq war ended, Iraq invaded its smaller neighbor Kuwait to control its large oil reserves. After diplomacy failed, the USA organized an international alliance to repel the Iraqi force. The Alliance dislodged the Iraqi army from Kuwait. However, before it retreated, the Iraqi military set over 700 oil wells on fire, devastating the region's environment.

In addition to leading to wars, the desire to control oil led to several civil conflicts. Iraq experiences constant tension over oil fields between the Shiites in the south, Sunni in the middle, and Kurds. Most of Iraq's oil fields are located in the north or the south, leaving the Sunnis with little access to oil. Similarly, in 2016, a group calling itself the Avengers attacked oil facilities in the Delta region of Nigeria. They demanded that the locals receive a share of the oil revenue and environmental remediation for decades of fossil fuel pollution.

Dependence on oil can lead to political instability. Hugo Chavez, Venezuela's president from 2002 to 2013, used oil money to improve education, healthcare, and infrastructure. He also used oil money to consolidate his political power and increase Venezuela's political influence. Chavez donated money to presidential candidates in Bolivia, Nicaragua, Paraguay, and Peru. He provided subsidized oil to his political allies, such as Cuba. His goal was to create a block of socialist countries in the region. Chavez used oil money to build political opposition to the USA and Western Europe.

Shortly after Nicolás Maduro was elected to succeed Chavez, who died from cancer in 2013, oil prices declined from $109 to $37 per barrel. Maduro could no longer pay for public services, infrastructure, or military, and the economy collapsed. In January 2019, with the county experiencing rising poverty, power shortages, and growing crime, the voters ousted him. However, he refused to leave, and Venezuela descended into a civil war causing over six million people to flee the country. Venezuela's political crisis highlights another problem with oil. Since petroleum prices wildly fluctuate, countries that depend on oil revenue often experience economic booms and busts.

Terrorist groups also used oil revenue to finance their campaigns. The Islamic State, a ruthless terrorist group, wrestled control of oil fields in northern Iraq and central Syria. They made between $8 to $10 million a month by smuggling oil through Turkey and used this money to pay their fighters and support local communities. Oil revenue allowed the Islamic State to expand its brutal crusade.

Al Qaeda also received funding from oil. Osama Bin Laden, its notorious leader who masterminded the September 11 attack on the Twin Towers and the Pentagon, received much of his wealth from petroleum. Recently, an arm of Al Qaeda made money by selling oil from Yemen in the midst of a civil war and used it to finance terrorist attacks in Paris and elsewhere.

The Iranian government also benefits from oil production. The Irani government is controlled by fundamental Muslims. It funnels some of its oil revenue to support terrorist organizations like Hezbollah in Lebanon and Hamas in Palestine. Around 70% of Iran's government revenue comes from exporting oil. Its oil revenue allows it to wield considerable political power over the region. It also utilizes government revenue from oil to develop its nuclear program. Iran claims that it is enriching uranium only to generate electricity. However, international observers believe that Iran is building nuclear weapons. Oil revenue allows Iran to spend over $18 billion a year on its military.

The Price of Petro

Our dependence on petroleum makes us vulnerable to fluctuations in its price. The 2000s provided a powerful illustration of how unstable petroleum prices can be. Oil price per barrel rose from $12.52 in 2002 to $133.88 in 2008. The sharpest increase occurred in the summer of 2008. That year, prices rose due to multiple supply shocks, a rise in demand by China, and speculations on oil.

In the mid-2000s, Iraq experienced armed conflicts among Shiites, Sunnis, and Kurds over controlling its oil fields. Trouble was brewing elsewhere. In February of 2008, Venezuela, South America's biggest oil producer, stopped selling oil to ExxonMobil due to a legal battle over nationalizing the company's properties. In Nigeria, rebels attacked fuel facilities along the Niger Delta and forced oil companies to halt production. Nigeria is Africa's top oil producer.

Conflicts in Iraq, Nigeria, and Venezuela reduced the global oil supply. At the time, the world economy was experiencing strong growth, leading to a sharp rise in demand for energy. Emerging giants like China and India needed more oil to sustain their rapid industrial growth. A depreciation in the dollar made things worse since oil traders demanded more dollars per barrel. The depreciation in the dollar raised prices in the USA and encouraged investors to invest in oil as a hedge against inflation. As oil prices continued to rise, investors started speculating on oil futures, further driving its price. Commodity futures provide a way to invest in oil or other commodities without purchasing them.

In the summer of 2008, the prices at US pumps topped $4 per gallon. Gasoline became such a financial burden that some employers restructured their work schedules so that workers only had to drive to work four or three days a week. Airlines struggled to cope with the high cost of fuel. Continental Airlines eliminated around 3,000 jobs and grounded sixty-seven aircraft. Then, the bubble burst. The US real estate market collapsed and the country entered its worst recession since the Great Depression. Oil prices collapsed. By December of 2008, the price per barrel fell to $41.1. Crude oil lost around 70% of its value in half a year.

The energy crisis of 2008 is only one example of a supply shock. The worst supply shock in history was the OPEC crisis of 1974. The OPEC boycott raised the price of gasoline by 350%. The crisis sent the economy into a tailspin. Similarly, when Saddam Hussein invaded Kuwait—a large petroleum producer—in 1990, he created a supply shock. In 2005, Hurricane Katrina shut down most rigs in the Gulf of Mexico, which produce over a third of US petroleum. As long as we depend on oil, our economy is vulnerable to world events outside our control.

CHAPTER 6: GASLIGHTING

Pay no attention to the man behind the curtain!
Noel Langley from *The Wizard of Oz*

In 2012, Hanson and Michael Rowe noticed a fetid stench rising from an abandoned gas well on their land in Kentucky. The fumes made them nauseous and short of breath. Earlier, the Rowes had agreed to let J.D. Carty Resources, a gas exploration company, drill for natural gas on their property. In exchange, J.D. Carty promised them 12.5% of the royalties and free gas. The company never paid the couple and abandoned the well without properly capping it.

This century, the USA has shifted from coal to natural gas as its primary source of electricity. In 2005, the USA generated 50% of its electricity from coal and 19% from natural gas. By 2019, the picture reversed. The USA produced 19% of its electricity from coal and 38% from natural gas. Many politicians heralded natural gas as clean energy. Indeed, natural gas creates less pollution than coal. However, burning natural gas still harms the environment, and using it at home is dangerous. Moreover, fracking bedrocks to extract natural gas causes air pollution, water pollution, habitat destruction, and earthquakes. While natural gas is cleaner, it is still harmful to people and the planet. This chapter discusses the advantages and disadvantages of using natural gas and explains why we should discontinue its use.

A Faultless Fuel?
Like coal and petroleum, natural gas is a fossil fuel. It forms underground from decaying organic material. Natural gas is composed of 70% to 90% methane, a gas with one carbon atom and four hydrogen atoms. It is flammable and may become explosive when mixed with air. It can also cause asphyxia by reducing the oxygen in closed spaces. In addition to methane, natural gas contains

hydrocarbons, carbon monoxide, water vapor, and trace amounts of other chemicals.

Like petroleum, natural gas has various uses. We use it to generate electricity, heat our homes, cook, and power vehicles. We can convert natural gas to liquefied natural gas (LNG) by cooling it to a liquid at about -260° Fahrenheit. LNG is more transportable than gas. Trucks and other large vehicles can use LNG as fuel.

In some ways, natural gas is a cleaner fuel than coal or petroleum. Unlike coal, natural gas does not contain mercury or lead. It has less sulfur dioxide and nitrogen oxide and creates less acid rain. Moreover, unlike coal and oil, natural gas does not emit soot. Soot consists of fine particles generated from the incomplete burning of fossil fuels. They cause respiratory and cardiovascular ailments such as bronchitis, asthma, and strokes.

Natural gas can potentially generate fewer greenhouse gases. It generates 117 pounds of carbon dioxide per million British Thermal Units (BTUs), a measure of energy. By comparison, coal generates 200, and petroleum produces 160 pounds of carbon dioxide per million BTUs. The natural gas industry proudly claims that the USA's carbon dioxide emissions fell by 21% since 2000, thanks chiefly to our increased use of natural gas instead of coal.

While US Democrats often criticize our use of coal and oil, natural gas receives bipartisan support. President Barack Obama, for instance, advocated for natural gas, claiming that its use decreases the emissions of greenhouse gases and reduces America's dependency on foreign fuels. The US extraction of natural gas grew by 38% under the Obama administration.

Natural gas is abundant in the USA. Using natural gas creates jobs in states like Texas, Pennsylvania, and North Dakota. Oil and gas companies employ people to discover, extract, transport, and use it. In 2017, the energy sector employed 6.4 million Americans—an increase of 5% from 2016, and most job growth was due to natural gas and renewable energy.

It is easy to see why natural gas appeals to politicians and consumers. It is more efficient than other fossil fuels, emits fewer pollutants, and reduces the US's dependence on foreign fuels. The USA has been the largest net importer of energy since the late 1950s. However, in 2017 the United States became an energy exporter for the first time in six decades, thanks to its increased use of natural gas. It is currently piping natural gas to Canada and Mexico.

However, natural gas has several dirty secrets. It is made predominantly from methane, which is a greenhouse gas. While methane does not last as long in the atmosphere as carbon dioxide, it warms the earth by more than twenty times as much as carbon dioxide. Oil and gas companies try to trap methane and burn it, but they are not always successful. It leaks into the atmosphere during the extraction, transportation, storage, and use of natural gas.

Until recently, most scientists assumed that under 1% of the methane from natural gas leaks. Since methane is a transparent gas, detecting leaks is difficult. A recent study, however, claims that the number is closer to 2%. This difference may seem trivial, but methane is a potent greenhouse gas. Even a trace amount of methane affects the earth's climate. While shifting from coal to natural gas may reduce carbon dioxide emissions, it increases methane emissions and may not help us manage climate change.

Natural gas also contains carbon monoxide. Carbon monoxide is highly toxic to humans and animals. It can cause nausea, confusion, and death. Around 50,000 people in the USA visit the emergency room yearly due to carbon monoxide poisoning, and at least 400 die. While natural gas is cleaner than other fossil fuels, it can still contain sulfur dioxide, nitrogen oxides, and other toxic compounds. These chemicals can leak into the air without being detected.

What the Frack?
One of the most concerning things about natural gas is its extraction. The USA extracts most of its gas using hydraulic fracturing, also called fracking. Fracking involves drilling a well deep into bedrock to reach a shale—a stratified sedimentary rock that forms from

compressed mud. The drill is then typically turned 90 degrees to drill horizontally through the shale. Next, the exploratory company shakes the drill or uses explosives to create fissures in the rock. Finally, the company injects the well with a mix of water, sand, benzene, and other chemicals to release the gas from the shale. The company then collects the natural gas and oil from the top of the well.

Fracking recently gained popularity, but it is scarcely a new technology. It was developed shortly after the Civil War. During the battle of Fredericksburg, Colonel Edward Roberts observed how firing artillery into a narrow canal caused the land around the explosion to fracture. Following the War, Roberts founded the Roberts Petroleum Torpedo Company. His company extracted oil by lowering a torpedo in an iron case into oil wells. After blowing up the explosive, it would fill the hole with water. This method helped substantially increase oil production.

In the 1940s, Standard Oil (now Amoco) and Halliburton improved on Roberts' technique by injecting a mixture of water, gelled gasoline, and sand into wells. Gas companies continued to improve the process and develop equipment to dig deeper. They began using it to extract natural gas. However, it was not until the twenty-first century that fracking gained popularity. In 2000, fracking accounted for just 7% of the US's natural gas production. By 2015, it accounted for 67%. Its production grew from 3.6 to 53 billion cubic feet per day.

The gas industry claims that fracking is safe, but there are significant concerns about the process. For starters, fracking requires a lot of water. It requires an average of 4 million gallons of water per well. There are around a million active wells in the USA, necessitating over 4 trillion gallons of water. Many of the wells are located in relatively dry areas and place considerable stress on the local water supply.

Gas companies inject water mixed with sand and various chemicals into the well to free the gas. This mix can seep into the watershed if the borehole is not sealed correctly or the drill reaches an aquifer. Consequently, the chemicals used in the process can accidentally pollute the local water supply. Since the chemicals used are considered proprietary information, it is impossible to know their potential harm. The Environmental Protection Agency identifies chemicals that companies might use for fracking. Many of them are toxic.

In addition to potentially polluting local watersheds, fracking releases potentially harmful pollutants into the air. Some methane invariably escapes during extraction, contributing to the greenhouse effect. Fracking also releases Volatile Organic Compounds (VOCs), tiny particles that can cause respiratory and cardiovascular health issues. Additionally, fracking releases nitrogen oxides, which can cause respiratory problems and acid rain.

Those who live close to the well often get exposed to toxins that can cause headaches, immunological issues, reproductive system defects, and cancer. A study of natural gas wells in Arkansas, Colorado, Pennsylvania, Ohio, and Wyoming found eight poisonous chemicals whose levels far exceeded recommended federal limits. These chemicals include benzene and formaldehyde, which can cause cancer.

The study discovered that the levels of benzene near natural gas wells were 35 to 770,000 times greater than normal. Similarly, hydrogen sulfide levels were 90 to 60,000 times above the federally recommended level. These high levels can cause respiratory irritation, fatigue, irritability, memory loss, and dizziness after merely an hour of exposure.

Fracking may create other issues besides pollution. Oil and gas companies purposefully shake the drill or use explosives to fracture the shale. Doing so can create minor earthquakes, which are supposed to register as 1.0 or lower on the Richter scale. Researchers, however, have linked fracking to more powerful earthquakes. A group of scientists from the Miami University of Ohio detected earthquakes from fracking that registered between 2.0 and 3.8.

In 2019, the United Kingdom banned fracking due to its concerns over earthquakes and environmental degradation. The United Kingdom's decision prompted France, Germany, Austria, the Netherlands, and other European nations to prohibit fracking as well.

Fracking would not be as harmful to the environment if it were better regulated. The federal government should require companies to reveal which chemicals they use for fracking and ban the use of highly toxic chemicals. Exploratory companies should properly seal unused gasoline wells. Local governments should require them to post a bond to cover the cost of capping the well. Finally, governments should not allow fracking close to populated areas.

The Roof is on Fire

Perhaps the scariest thing about natural gas is not that its extraction, transportation, and consumption lead to pollution but that Americans increasingly use natural gas in their homes. 48% of homes in the USA use natural gas for heating and cooking. In 2020, natural gas accounted for 42% of residential energy consumption. While natural gas is commonplace in cold states, its use is spreading throughout the country.

Most Americans view natural gas positively. 76% of Americans view natural gas favorably, compared to 51% who view oil and 39% who view coal favorably. In fact, according to a Pew survey, 72% of Americans support expanding the use of natural gas. The survey, which polled residents of twenty countries, found that in all but two countries, Sweden and the Netherlands, most people support using more gas.

Many people find natural gas appealing because it warms their homes quickly and is cheaper than electricity in many places. In 2021, Americans spent $746 to heat homes with natural gas and $1,268 with electricity. Developers sell many new homes in so-called natural gas communities. The name implies that natural gas makes the property desirable.

While there are advantages to using natural gas in residential neighborhoods, it is also unsafe. As noted, it is made primarily from methane and can cause asphyxia by displacing oxygen. Small quantities of methane can cause headaches and fatigue. In large concentrations, methane can cause vomiting, loss of consciousness, and, in rare cases, death. For instance, in 2007, five people died from a methane leak on a dairy farm in Virginia.

Methane is also highly flammable when its concentration reaches 5% of the air. In 1937, 295 students died in New London, Texas, from a gas explosion at school. The number of victims was several times larger than the 2007 Virginia Tech shooting, the deadliest school shooting in history. The force of the explosion tore up a two-ton concrete block and crushed a car parked 200 feet away. A 1995 explosion in Westminster, Maryland, damaged around fifty homes and forced 300 people to evacuate.

While big explosions from methane are uncommon, house fires from natural gas are commonplace. The National Fire Protection Association estimates that, on average, 4,200 homes burn annually because of natural gas. These fires cause an average of forty deaths every year and millions of dollars in property damage. House fires can spread across a natural gas community and damage multiple homes.

Natural gas also contains toxic carbon monoxide. CO attacks the central nervous system, causing headaches, dizziness, nausea, confusion, seizures, and, sometimes, hallucinations. Carbon monoxide poisoning kills over 400 people in the USA every year. In 2021, a family of seven died in their sleep in Moorhead, Minnesota from gas poisoning. The next day, a family of eight was hospitalized due to carbon monoxide poisoning in Shakopee, Minnesota.

Google the words "family carbon monoxide poisoning," and you will find dozens of stories of families who have lost members or gone to the hospital because of CO poisoning. The scariest thing about carbon monoxide is that it causes people to lose consciousness or fall asleep. If you have a CO leak at home, there is a good chance that you will never wake up to respond to it.

In 2019, Berkley, California, became the first city in the USA to ban the use of natural gas. The city requires developers to switch to other forms of energy by 2029. San Francisco, Seattle, Denver, and New York, have banned or discouraged the use of natural gas in new homes. Many European cities also prohibited the use of natural gas for heating.

Policymakers often present natural gas as a bridge fuel, a more environmentally friendly alternative to oil and coal that we should use until we build up renewable energy capacity. If natural gas is a bridge fuel, we must cross this bridge quickly. While it does emit less pollution, it is unclear whether natural gas causes less climatic instability than oil. Moreover, its extraction and use are harmful to the environment and humans. We must also better regulate fracking, require gas companies to properly seal inactive gas wells, and discourage people from using natural gas in their homes by taxing it or using other incentives.

The Land of Broken Promises
In the 2012 film *Promised Land*, Matt Damon plays a character named Steve. Steve's job is to win drilling rights from landowners in a struggling Pennsylvania town. The community seems receptive until a local high school teacher questions the safety of the drilling process. An environmental advocate named Dustin arrives in town and begins campaigning against drilling. He explains how his family lost their Nebraska farm after their livestock died due to gas exploration. Steve's company sends him a picture of Dustin's farm in Louisiana. Steve exposes the deception and wins the town's support. He later discovers that his firm sent Dustin to discredit the environmental movement.

While the movie *Promised Land* is fictional, it highlights two things about gas companies. First, they make promises that they do not fulfill to struggling landowners. Secondly, they work hard to control the narrative and cast natural gas as eco-friendly. The term natural implies something good. In reality, natural gas is harmful to the planet and people. Gas companies fail to pay many landowners who allow drilling on their land. They also regularly abandon gas wells when they are no longer economically viable. Inactive wells can spew toxins and devalue the land. The US alone had more than 3.2 million abandoned oil and gas wells in 2018.

The EPA estimates that abandoned fields spewed 281 kilotons of methane into the atmosphere in 2018. Orphaned wells can contaminate watersheds and make the water supply unsafe for drinking and agriculture. The US government estimates that it would take between $60 billion to $435 billion to plug all the abandoned oil and gas wells in the USA.

Like the Rowe family in Kentucky, many landowners have abandoned natural gas wells on their properties. Thousands of others who live near natural gas fields have to deal with benzene, hydrogen sulfide, and other pollutants. Thousands more who use natural gas in their homes suffer from gas poisoning or fires made worse by natural gas. Natural gas sounds like a faultless fuel, but it comes with many costs. Like coal and petroleum, we should strive to phase out its use within a few decades.

CHAPTER 7: ANALYZING ALTERNATIVES

History teaches us that men and nations behave wisely once they have exhausted all other alternatives. Abba Eban

Every spring, dead fish appear on the beaches of the Gulf of Mexico. Sometimes, the rotting fish cover the sand, and the stench is unbearable. They are the victims of what is known as a dead zone, an area of low or no oxygen created by algal bloom. These blooms occur when algae feed on the phosphorous and nitrogen from fertilizers introduced to the Gulf of Mexico by the Mississippi River. When the algae die, they consume the oxygen in the water. Fish, shrimp, and other marine animals must swim away from the area or perish. Escape, however, is not simple—the dead zone can reach 8,000 square miles or roughly the size of New Jersey.

The Mississippi watershed covers roughly a third of the contingent US and flows through numerous farms. US farmers use over 20 million tons of chemical fertilizers for crops like corn and soy. Corn is America's biggest crop, but most of it is not for human consumption. Instead, we use it as animal feed and produce a biofuel called ethanol. While ethanol emits fewer greenhouse gases, we must use more fertilizers, pesticides, and water to produce it, creating environmental problems down the stream. Ethanol is often presented a sustainable alternative to fossil fuels, but it harms the environment. This chapter explores alternatives to gasoline and discusses why we should not use most of them and why the only sustainable solution is to use electricity to fuel vehicles.

The Many Forms of Fossil Fuels

There are other alternatives to gasoline, including other products from petroleum and natural gas such as diesel fuel, propane, and LNG. Some herald these fuels as more environmentally friendly than gasoline. However, these alternative fuels still emit greenhouse gases and have many shortcomings.

Some vehicles use diesel instead of gasoline. Like gasoline, diesel is a petroleum product. Unlike gasoline engines, diesel engines do not use an electric spark to cause the fuel to combust. Instead, diesel engines compress the fuel inside the engine's cylinder until it ignites from the pressure. Diesel fuel is more concentrated than gasoline and emits more carbon dioxide per gallon. However, diesel vehicles provide significantly higher mileage per gallon. Diesel engines also produce less carbon monoxide.

Diesel vehicles are uncommon in the United States, except for large trucks. By contrast, about half of the cars in Europe operate on diesel. Recently, engineers were able to develop cleaner diesel fuel. Their goal was to have the engine completely burn the fuel by premixing it with air and using a computer to better time the cylinders' combustions. These improvements led many, including some environmental groups like the Sierra Club, to claim that modern diesel cars are cleaner than gas cars.

The jury is still out on which fuel is eco-friendlier. While diesel engines generate less carbon monoxide and carbon dioxide than gasoline engines, they can emit 25 to 400 times more particulates. Particulates can cause eye irritations, respiratory diseases, and cardiovascular diseases. Moreover, many of the past claims about diesel come from falsified data. Volkswagen, the world's biggest producer of diesel cars, installed devices in many of its diesel cars to detect when they were inspected for emissions. These devices changed the engine performance to show less emission. Volkswagen admitted to installing these devices in about 11 million vehicles. Even if diesel cars are cleaner than in the past, they still create air pollution and emit greenhouse gases. They also appear to produce more nitrogen oxide on the road than in a controlled environment where regulators typically test cars.

Diesel fuel is, at best, a slightly cleaner alternative to gasoline. Even if it is cleaner, it is still a petroleum-based fuel. If we switch to diesel, humanity will still need to deal with all the environmental and socioeconomic problems that exploring, extracting, and transporting petroleum create.

Propane, another proposed alternative to gasoline, is also a fossil fuel. People use propane for outdoor grills, waste treatment, weed control, and small turbines. Propane burns cleaner than gasoline or diesel, and scientists believe we can use it as car fuel. It is less efficient than gasoline as it produces 27% less energy per gallon, but because it is lower in carbon content, it creates less greenhouse gas. It may also lead to longer engine life, especially in high-use vehicles such as taxis and commercial trucks. Propane is cheaper than gasoline, and we can use some of the existing infrastructures for gas to deliver it to drivers. Unlike gasoline or diesel, propane does not emit sulfur dioxide, nitrogen oxides, or methane.

Although propane is cleaner than gasoline, it has never gained significant traction as a fuel for transportation. Manufacturers have only produced a handful of propane-powered cars. Some school buses also run on propane. Since propane has a lower density than gasoline or diesel, vehicles that run on propane have a shorter driving range and must fuel up more frequently. While we can use propane in gasoline-powered engines, we will have to build storage tanks, specialized pumps, and metering systems to deliver propane while keeping it pressurized.

Although propane is slightly better for the environment than gasoline, it still emits carbon dioxide. Fume from propane can cause asphyxia. Furthermore, its exploration, extraction, and transportation lead to similar problems as gasoline. Propane provides some benefits. However, we must invest in the infrastructure to produce and deliver it. Even if governments were interested in propane, which they are not, it would only provide a short-term solution.

Liquified Natural Gas is another fossil fuel we could use as an alternative to gasoline. As noted previously, some large vehicles use LNG. However, we can expand its use to smaller vehicles as well. LNG produces half as much carbon dioxide per unit of energy as gasoline. As the price of natural gas falls, LNG could become cheaper to use. LNG is cleaner than gasoline or diesel—it generates fewer toxins and does not emit soot.

However, LNG has multiple drawbacks. Countries must build the infrastructure to liquefy, transfer, and store LNG to utilize it. While natural gas is cleaner than gasoline, it is not a clean fuel, and we should not use it. It emits carbon dioxide, carbon monoxide, sulfur dioxide, nitrogen oxides, and other pollutants. Moreover, natural gas is composed of methane—a potent greenhouse gas. Methane often leaks during the extraction and transportation of natural gas. Furthermore, as explained earlier, extracting natural gas through fracking can lead to water pollution, air pollution, and earthquakes.

A Tipsy Trip

Not all fuels are fossil fuels. Biofuels come from living organisms. While biofuels seem to provide sustainable alternatives to gasoline, they have multiple drawbacks. Therefore, we should not invest heavily in biofuels. Humanity must focus on producing EVs.

Ethanol is the most widely used biofuel. It is an alcohol derived from plant-based sugar. Producers derive ethanol by fermenting corn, sugar cane, sugar beets, sorghum, barley, or grass. Global ethanol production more than doubled between 2007 and 2019, with the USA and Brazil leading the way. The USA is the world's largest ethanol producer. It produces most of its ethanol from corn. Brazil, the second-largest producer, uses sugar. The USA and Brazil produce more ethanol than the rest of the world combined.

Putting alcohol in your gas tank may seem odd, but if you live in the USA, you are already doing this. The Energy Independence and Security Act of 2007 allows gas companies to mix up to 10% ethanol with gasoline. A mixture of gas and 10% ethanol is known as gasohol. Over 98% of "gasoline" sold in the USA is gasohol. A typical car can run on gasohol without modifications.

One way to use more ethanol is by building cars with flex engines. Flex engines can use different blends of gasoline and ethanol, with up to 85% ethanol. Over 22 million vehicles in the USA have flex engines, representing around 8% of the vehicles on the road. Yet, less than 3% of gas stations in the USA serve E85.

In Brazil, over 73% of all vehicles and 90% of new cars have flex engines. The Brazilian government has invested heavily in ethanol refineries and infrastructure. Brazil produces most of its ethanol from sugarcane, a more efficient source than corn. Brazil produces ethanol from sugar since its tropical climate is ideal for sugar production. It is the largest exporter of sugar.

Gas companies add ethanol to gasoline for two reasons. Since ethanol is cheaper than petroleum, they save money by doing so. Additionally, ethanol increases the fuel's octane, which means that it makes it more stable. There are also environmental reasons to support ethanol. A 2019 study by the US Department of Agriculture found that corn-based ethanol emits 39% fewer greenhouse gases than gasoline.

Ethanol comes from plants, is non-toxic, and is biodegradable. Since plants photosynthesize—they convert carbon dioxide into oxygen and energy. The carbon dioxide that E85 generates is partly offset by the plants that produce it. Moreover, since most nations can produce ethanol locally, it creates domestic jobs, supports farming communities, and reduces the need to import fuels.

While there are many advantages to using ethanol, there are more disadvantages. Ethanol is corrosive and can damage engines in the long haul. Also, E85 has higher evaporative emissions, which causes smog and ground-level ozone. While E85 has higher octane than gasoline, it also has a lower fuel efficiency, meaning that flex engines get fewer miles per gallon.

Increasing our reliance on ethanol also requires clearing animal habitats for agriculture, reducing plant diversity, and using more pesticides, herbicides, and fertilizers. Pesticides and herbicides are toxic to birds, fish, beneficial insects, and non-target plants. These toxic chemicals can cause cardiovascular diseases, respiratory diseases, and cancer. Fertilizers, as noted at the beginning of the chapter, can wash into the sea and create dead zones.

Using crops such as corn and grains for fuel makes our food supply more vulnerable to fluctuations in demand for energy. Corn provides over 96% of animal feed in the USA. Therefore, diverting corn to produce ethanol will likely raise the price of meat. Food manufacturers use corn syrup as an additive for candy, cereal, and an array of processed foods. Diverting more corn to produce ethanol will also raise the cost of various groceries.

It is not surprising, given its shortcomings, that ethanol is not used extensively outside of the USA and Brazil. Since the USA has many corn farmers, politicians gain support by subsidizing corn-based ethanol. Between 1980 and 2011, the US government gave $45 billion in tax breaks to ethanol producers to reduce the cost of ethanol by 45% per gallon and keep it competitive. These subsidies exist in addition to farm subsidies and low-interest government loans for farmers. Without government support, corn-based ethanol would not be economically competitive.

Supporting sugar-based ethanol helps the Brazilian government gain political support from sugar farmers. However, Brazil's love affair with ethanol is waning. A recent article in Bloomberg Magazine revealed that Brazilians are purchasing more EVs, causing the demand for sugar to drop. Brazil and the US should eliminate their subsidies for ethanol and focus on EVs.

Ethanol is not the only alcohol-based fuel. In the 1990s, the US federal government promoted methanol as a fuel. Like ethanol, methanol is a type of alcohol. Methanol contains one carbon, while ethanol contains two carbons per molecule. The Energy Policy Act of 1992 recognized methanol as a viable alternative to gas. It is cheaper and less flammable than gasoline.

Methanol has many of the same shortcomings as ethanol, but it is worse than ethanol in two ways. Methanol is highly toxic. Exposure to methanol can cause headaches, nausea, vomiting, seizures, and blindness. Additionally, methanol is more corrosive than ethanol and can damage the engine hoses and other parts. Thankfully, the USA phased out the use of methanol. Although, some developing countries like China still use it.

Better Biofuels

Other biofuels may be better for the environment than ethanol or methanol, but they too have shortcomings. While we can consider using these biofuels to some extent in the future, our focus should remain on producing EVs.

Biodiesel also seems like a promising alternative to gasoline. Scientists produce biodiesel by separating plant or animal oil into methyl esters and glycerin. We use glycerin to create various products, such as soap, and blend methyl esters with diesel to produce biofuel. Today, more than 78% of all new diesel vehicles can use a biofuel blend, consisting of up to 20% biodiesel mixed with petroleum diesel. However, cars that run entirely on biodiesel require a different engine.

Biodiesels emit less pollution and greenhouse gases than gas when burned. We can produce them domestically, creating local jobs and reducing the economy's dependence on imports. Biodiesel surged in popularity at the beginning of this century. In the USA, we increased biodiesel production from merely 10 million gallons in 2001 to over 2 billion gallons in 2016. The US government subsidizes the production of biofuels through the Renewable Fuels Standard Program. Other nations like Brazil, France, Indonesia, and Germany also support biodiesels. Nonetheless, US biodiesel production began falling in 2016 because of its limitations. By 2019, it was down to 1.81 billion gallons.

Research by the Environmental Protection Agency suggests that biofuels have several undesirable effects. As with ethanol, we will need to replace forests with agricultural lands. Doing so could increase greenhouse emissions and pressure on water supplies. We will also need to use more pesticides, herbicides, and fertilizers to produce biofuels on a large scale. While mixing diesel with biofuels makes it eco-friendlier, growing the plants needed to produce biofuels creates multiple environmental and economic problems.

We can also produce biofuel from algae. Oil produced from algae has several advantages over other biofuels. Alga is versatile and can grow in various climates. It can be grown in open ponds or closed photo-bioreactors and does not need to use farmland. Algae grow fast and have high per-acre productivity. Creating fuel from algae does not divert crops from our food supply, and they do not require pesticides. Moreover, they remove carbon dioxide from the atmosphere through photosynthesis. So, while the production of other biofuels may be carbon neutral or carbon positive (meaning adding carbon to the atmosphere), algal biofuel reduces the amount of carbon dioxide in the atmosphere. Algal oil does not have the drawbacks of ethanol or biodiesel.

In 2009, Sapphire Energy produced the first algal-powered car dubbed Algaeus in San Francisco. Despite the many advantages of algal biofuel, the technology never bloomed. After fifteen years of research and millions of dollars in investment, the green technology sector largely abandoned this idea. Producing algal oil on a large scale requires a lot of water, carbon dioxide, and fertilizers. For instance, research shows that using algal oil to power 10% of the vehicles in Europe requires ponds that are three times the size of Belgium. Unfortunately, it is too expensive to make. Furthermore, it is unclear whether we can produce it on a large scale.

There may still be hope for algae oil. Recently, researchers at the University of Utah developed a method to extract algal oil that requires less energy and time. However, creating enough algal fuel to power our cars will require an extensive infrastructure of labs, ponds, pipelines, and delivery systems. At this point, algal biofuel is far more expensive per unit of energy than gasoline or electricity. With the cost of electricity from sustainable energy falling, there is no reason to wait and see if algal biofuel could, one day, become useful. Algal biofuel might play a minor role in tomorrow's sustainable energy economy.

Fool Cells
Hydrogen fuel cells seem like another promising alternative to gasoline. They work like batteries by separating hydrogen atoms into positive ions (positively charged nuclei without electrons) in the cathode and negative ions (negatively charged nuclei with two electrons) in the anode. The cathode is positive, and the anode is the

negative side of the battery. The positive ions travel directly to the cathode through the partition that separates the two sides. However, the electron must travel through the engine to reach the cathode, thus providing electricity to the vehicle. When the electrons reach the cathode, the negative and positive ions combine with oxygen ions, forming water and heat.

Hydrogen is the most abundant element in nature. However, it does not exist on its own on earth. To supply hydrogen to fuel cells, we must first separate water into its two elements, hydrogen, and oxygen. This process requires a lot of energy and may increase greenhouse gas emissions, depending on how we create the electricity to split the hydrogen. If this energy comes from coal or petroleum, it will increase greenhouse gas emissions. If it comes from natural gas, it can modestly decrease emissions. Although, extracting natural gas harms the environment. If it comes from renewable energy, it can lower emissions by 90%. Hydrogen fuel cells benefit the environment only if we commit to producing electricity from sustainable energy.

Shifting to fuel cells requires rebuilding our transportation infrastructure. To use hydrogen as fuel, we must build a system of pipelines, trucks, storage facilities, compressors, and dispensers. Unlike gasoline, hydrogen must remain highly compressed while transported and stored, and it can leak if not handled properly. A few densely populated regions, including Southern California, have the infrastructure to deliver hydrogen fuel. However, transporting hydrogen to rural areas or developing countries is prohibitively expensive.

A few automakers, such as Toyota, produce fuel cell cars. However, they are far more expensive than EVs. Toyota Mirai starts at around $60,000 compared to Tesla's popular Model 3, which starts at $35,000, or Hong Guang Mini EV, which costs $5,000. Elon Musk calls fuel cells "fool cells." Currently, there is limited interest among automakers, investors, or governments in this expensive technology.

We should not use fuel cells to power our transportation, but we might utilize them to store energy. To shift to sustainable energy, we must find large-scale solutions to store electricity. Renewable energy is intermittent—the sun only shines during the day, and the wind does not always blow. Power companies could use excess electricity from sustainable energy to break water into hydrogen and store the hydrogen in tanks. Then, they could convert the hydrogen into electricity using large fuel cells when they have a shortage of electricity.

While fuels such as LNG, propane, ethanol, biodiesel, hydrogen, and algae oil may seem promising, their costs exceed their benefits. In some cases, these costs are hard to see. For instance, producing fuel from corn seems like a sustainable solution, but it leads to environmental issues such as dead zones. Thus, we should focus on EV technology. It is cheaper and more beneficial to the environment than any other alternative fuel.

SUMMARY OF PART II

Humanity uses fossil fuels to generate electricity, power machines, create heat, and make various materials. Fossil fuels are efficient, but they harm the environment. Coal is dangerous to extract, emits greenhouse gases, and releases toxins like mercury and particulates. The extraction and use of petroleum emit greenhouse gases, create economic instability, lead to political conflict, and generate funds for terrorist activities. Natural gas creates less pollution than oil or coal. However, fracking, the process used to extract it, pollutes watersheds, releases toxins, and can cause earthquakes. Other fuels, such as ethanol and biodiesel, may look promising, but they also strain the environment and are inferior to using electricity to power vehicles. Therefore, we must stop using fossil fuels and focus on developing a sustainable energy economy.

PART III: TOWARD SUSTAINABILITY

Image by matthiasboeckel found on https://pixabay.com

CHAPTER 8: HERE COMES THE SUN

Ô, Sunlight! The most precious gold to be found on Earth.
Roman Payne

Remeza and her three friends had spent most of their lives in the small village of Ambakivao in Madagascar. However, after signing up for an innovative program sponsored by the World Wildlife Fund, they embarked on a journey that would forever change their lives and community. The four friends traveled to Barefoot College in India, where, alongside 140 other women from Africa, they spent half a year learning how to install and maintain photovoltaic solar panels. Upon returning to Madagascar, the women installed solar panels in their villages and nearby villages. Throughout Africa, these so-called solar grandmothers bring solar-generated electricity to local communities. Most of these places never had electricity.

The solar grandmothers provide an example of how solar energy spreads. Worldwide, companies and governments are installing new solar panels. We can install solar panels almost anywhere. In Cochin, India, the government installed solar panels on airport roofs. The Netherlands embedded solar panels on its bicycle paths. China installed solar panels on floats in lakes. In Chornobyl, the site of the world's worst nuclear disaster, the government converted abandoned lots into solar energy farms. Solar energy is the fastest-growing form of energy and the cheapest. This chapter will explain how solar energy works and why it should become the dominant form of energy in the future.

The Dawn of a New Day

Switching from gasoline cars to EVs will not lead to sustainability unless we also generate electricity from sustainable energy. If we continue using coal and natural gas to produce electricity, charging EVs will lead to the use of harmful fossil fuels. Our goal should be to stop producing electricity from fossil fuels by the middle of the century and switch to renewable and nuclear energy. This book will explain why we need nuclear power in Chapter 11. Recently, solar energy became the cheapest source per unit of energy, making it feasible to focus on renewable energy with solar energy as the dominant source.

At the start of the twenty-first century, supplying most of our electricity from renewable energy seemed like a pie in the sky. While there was widespread awareness about sustainability back then, the growth in renewable energies was slow due to their high cost. In 2001, less than 11% of the electricity in the USA came from renewable energy, mostly from hydroelectricity. Hydroelectricity requires damming a river and running the water through a generator. It is not a sustainable solution since it disrupts local ecosystems by blocking rivers and flooding regions. Additionally, the number of available locations for dams is limited.

At the start of the century, the USA and other governments focused on developing biofuels like ethanol. As discussed in the previous chapter, most biofuels are not environmentally friendly. Solar and wind energy presented a sliver in our energy profile. The percentage of electricity from renewable resources was actually decreasing. The US federal government elected to subsidize "clean" coal and natural gas to increase our capacity to generate electricity and reduce our dependence on foreign fuels.

Things rapidly changed in favor of renewable energy. In the 2010s, solar became cheaper to produce per kilowatt than any fossil fuels thanks to technological advancements. Over a decade, solar energy went from one of the most expensive forms of energy to the least costly. It became cheaper than coal and natural gas. Wind power, discussed in the next chapter, also became cheaper than most fossil fuels.

The US solar energy production grew from around 1,000 megawatts in 2011 to 87,000 by 2020. Within a decade, solar energy increased from a fraction of a percent to 2.3% of electricity produced in the USA. Solar panels started appearing on rooftops, lots, and fields throughout the country. Wind and solar energy capacity increased exponentially despite limited government support. The rise in solar energy is not limited to the USA. China, the world's second-biggest economy, installed 48.2 gigawatts of solar energy in 2020, or enough to power over 35 million homes. The European Union added 19.6 gigawatts of solar energy in 2020. After a modest start, we saw a rapid rise in the use of solar energy. The future looks bright for solar energy.

Panel Discussion

Engineers can convert sunlight into electricity using photovoltaic (PV) solar panels or concentrated solar power (CSP). Solar panels are devices that trap sunlight and use it to agitate electrons. People install solar panels on rooftops, empty lots, and fields. CSP plants use mirrors to focus light onto a tower, causing a liquid in a tank to turn to steam and power a generator.

CSP is a relatively new technology, invented by an Italian professor in 1968. Solar panels have existed for longer. Charles Fritts, a US inventor, developed the first solar cell in 1883 by coating selenium with a thin layer of gold. His solar cells converted one to two percent of solar radiation into electricity. Five years later, inventor Edward Weston received two patents to develop solar cells.

For nearly a century, solar panels were merely a scientific curiosity. However, surging energy prices in the 1970s led Congress to pass the Solar Energy Research, Development, and Demonstration Act of 1974. The Act accelerated the development of photovoltaic panels. Interest in solar energy waned during the 1980s, when energy prices were low, but rose again in the 1990s due to concerns about sustainability. In the twenty-first century, the use of solar panels surged. Now, almost a century and a half after Fritts developed the first solar cell, solar energy provides the most cost-effective way to produce electricity.

Solar panels contain many solar cells. These cells divide into two layers of silicon; one negatively charged layer, called N-type, with excess electrons, and a second positively charged layer, the P-type. When the photons in sunlight hit the N-type layer, it energizes some of the electrons and causes them to travel through a conductive strip to the P-type layer, thus releasing electricity.

Companies and local governments can use abandoned lots and shopping plazas to install solar energy farms. Unlike power plants, dams, or windmills, which usually deliver electricity to homes and factories from miles away, developers can place solar panels near consumers.

Solar energy is the fastest-growing source of electricity in the US due to its rising efficiency and accessibility. Yet, solar panels only convert a fraction of the light that hits them into electricity. In 2010, solar panels converted around 12% of the light they absorbed into electricity. By 2020, the conversion rate went up to 19%. Scientists theorize that we can convert up to 30% of solar radiation into electricity using silicon panels. 30% is probably not the upper limit. Some companies started experimenting with multi-junction panels that are composed of multiple materials. These panels could convert up to 47% of sunlight into electricity.

In addition to raising the conversion rate of solar panels, companies are improving the production and installation of panels. Like most manufactured goods, solar panels are subject to economies of scale. As we manufacture more solar panels, the cost per panel decreases. Over time, engineers find ways to produce solar panels more efficiently. Solar panel manufacturers learn by doing.

As the demand for solar panels rises, so does the need for installers. The Bureau of Labor Statistics (BLS) projects that solar panel installers will be the third-fastest-growing occupation in the United States between 2019 and 2029. It predicts a 51% increase in demand for installers this decade. The fastest-growing profession in the USA, with 61% projected growth, will be wind turbine technicians. Green energy will create many new domestic jobs.

A Thousand Splendid Reflections of the Sun
The second form of solar energy is Concentrated Solar Power. A CSP plant consists of thousands of large mirrors and a tower filled with liquid. Early CSP systems used water, but now they more commonly

use molten salt since it is less volatile and can store more energy. The mirrors reflect the light onto the tower. The extreme heat created from the concentrated light turns the liquid in the tower's tank into pressurized steam that flows through turbines. The steam-powered turbines connect to a generator. After going through the turbines, the liquid cools, condenses, and flows back to the tower. Modern CSP plants store energy inside the molten salt as heat during the daytime and use that heat to produce electricity at night. A CSP plant in Nevada uses 10,000 mirrors and molten salt to generate 110 megawatt-hours of electricity. It provides electricity to 75,000 homes.

CSP plants can produce a lot of energy, but they have limitations. We can only build plants away from population centers. Their location must have ample land and sunlight. Consequently, most CSP plants are in deserts. Countries built CSP plants in the Southwest USA, North Africa, the Middle East, and West China. By contrast, we can install solar panels almost anywhere. However, because they generate less energy than a CSP plant, they are typically only used for local energy production.

The use of solar energy is increasing globally, and China is leading the charge. In 2019, China generated 32% of the world's solar capacity. In fact, China leads the world in producing solar power, wind energy, and hydroelectricity. It is the world's top producer of renewable energy. The USA needs to invest more in renewable energy. It must do so to manage climate instability and to remain competitive with China in this emergent technology.

Solar energy has some handicaps. For starters, the amount of solar energy available varies by region. Solar energy is abundant in lower latitudes, especially in deserts. There is far less solar energy available near the earth's poles. Solar energy also varies by season. Solar panels may work well for towns and suburbs where each house can have them but are less effective in large, densely populated cities with limited space. Finally, panels break and must be replaced about every twenty-five years. Despite its drawbacks, solar energy should become our primary source of electricity since it is the most abundant and cheapest energy.

A Bright Future

In the future, we should drive EVs powered by sustainable electricity. Our primary source of electricity should be solar energy for five reasons. First, solar power is inexpensive. A 2020 Outlook Report by the International Energy Agency revealed that solar energy is now the cheapest source of electricity in history. It is cheaper to produce a megawatt of electricity from solar panels than from fossil fuels, nuclear energy, or other renewable resources. Moreover, the cost of solar energy will continue to decrease by as much as 65% over the next two decades. It makes sense to invest in solar energy because it helps control climatic instability and is the least expensive source of electricity.

Second, solar energy is nearly limitless. Every hour, 430 quintillion Joules of energy from the sun reach the earth. That is 430 with eighteen zeroes after it! It is enough to meet humanity's needs thousands of times over. With our current technology, 1.2% of the Sahara Desert could generate enough solar energy to provide our global demand. As technology improves and we learn how to convert more radiation into electricity, we will need even less space to meet our energy demand using solar power.

Third, we can install solar energy almost anywhere. We can build giant solar farms or build mini solar panels. The Bhadla Solar Park in India, the world's largest solar farm, has over 10 million panels, covers 14,000 acres, and produces over 2 gigawatts of energy. A gigawatt of energy can provide electricity to about 750,000 homes. We can also use mini solar panels to power electronics such as cell phones, watches, cameras, drones, and camping equipment.

Solar panels could be pervasive in the future. We can install them on rooftops to power our homes, place them on our electronics to charge when we are outside, and affix them to our EVs to help energize them. A Dutch company called Lightyear has designed cars with integrated solar panels, which charge the battery while driving.

The panels reduce but do not eliminate the need to plug in the vehicle. The company estimates that its cars could ride for 725 kilometers (450 miles) on a single charge.

Fourth, solar energy has fewer drawbacks than other sources of sustainable energy. Wind energy, for instance, is clean, but wind turbines require a lot of space, create noise, and kill birds. Geothermal plants have a limited capacity, are expensive, and often emit pollutants like sulfur dioxide. By contrast, solar panels are inexpensive, create no pollution, do not produce noise, and are safe for the environment. The next chapter delineates the advantages and shortcomings of other renewable energies.

Lastly, solar energy can solve the energy crisis in developing countries. Other forms of sustainable energy, such as nuclear power and hydroelectricity, require large-scale construction and a lot of knowledge to build. Solar panels are so simple to install that we can teach everyone how to do it. India trained grandmothers to install solar panels in their poor African villages. Solar energy could have a universal reach that benefits both the rich and the poor.

Governments should encourage the production of solar energy. They should incentivize homeowners to install solar panels using tax credits and grants. Solar panels are becoming more economical, but they require a sizable investment. Government should also invest in smart grids. Smart grids allow consumers to track how much electricity they use each hour and make wiser decisions about their energy consumption. They also allow homeowners and businesses to sell electricity to the grid. Residents who install solar panels can sell electricity to the grid in the daytime when the sun is shining and reduce their electric bills. Solar and wind energies should be the primary sources of electricity in the future. However, we should also utilize other renewable energies in regions where they are cost-effective.

CHAPTER 9: ANYWHERE THE WIND BLOWS

The breath of life is in the sunlight and the hand of life is in the
wind.
Kahlil Gibran

The Netherlands is known for its tulips, cheese, wooden clogs, bicycle
lanes, and cannabis. Although, is there anything more Dutch than
the windmills that adorn its countryside? The Dutch once used these
windmills to grind grain and pump water from the lowlands into
rivers. Over a quarter of the Netherlands is below sea level, so the
country built a complex system of dikes, barriers, and windmill-
operated pumps to protect itself from floods. Although visitors can
still see historical windmills throughout the country, the Dutch focus
on modern wind turbines. These gigantic turbines are not only
helping the Netherlands meet its energy needs, but they are also
helping the country combat climate change.

Towering at a breathtaking 853 feet above Rotterdam's port,
about the height of the Golden Gate Bridge, are massive wind
turbines. Their blades are 722 feet in diameter, about the length of
two football fields. Each turbine is capable of supplying 16,000
households with electricity. As astonishing as these colossal turbines
are, Vestas Wind Systems is already building taller and more
efficient turbines, which could each supply enough electricity for
20,000 households. When it comes to wind energy, the sky is the
limit. This chapter discusses the future of wind energy and other
forms of renewable energy. While solar energy should be the primary
energy in the future, additional renewable energies can also play an
important role.

The Wind of Change
Solar and wind energies are interconnected. Solar energy causes
winds that we can use to harvest wind energy. Winds are the
movements of air caused by uneven heating and planetary rotation.
The earth absorbs a lot of sunlight near the equator and converts

most of it into heat. Warm air from the equator expands, rises, and moves toward the poles, while cool, dense air flows toward the equator to replace the heated air. Because of the earth's rotation, warm air does not move directly poleward. Instead, it circulates counter-clockwise in cells in the Northern Hemisphere and clockwise in cells in the Southern Hemisphere.

Wind cells create consistent winds. For instance, trade winds move westward around the thirtieth latitude. Westerlies move eastward in mid-latitudes. Easterlies move from east to west near the poles. Prevailing winds influence climate, create waves, and drive ocean currents. For example, the Gulf Stream, which brings warm waters from the Caribbean to Europe, is driven by Westerlies in the Atlantic Ocean. Wind, currents, and waves carry tremendous energy. This energy can be converted into electricity using wind turbines, buoys, attenuators, and other devices that capture kinetic energy.

Wind power is one of the oldest forms of energy used by humanity. People used wind power to propel boats along the Nile River as early as 5,000 BC. By 200 BC, people in China and the Middle East were using windmills to grind grain. Traders and crusaders brought wind energy technology from the Middle East to Europe. The Dutch quickly embraced the technology and used it to grind grain and drain lowlands. Other European kingdoms also utilized windmills.

While wind power has a rich history, modern wind turbines are very different from their rustic predecessors. For starters, they are colossal. In 2020, the average wind turbine stood 295 feet tall, about the same height as the Statue of Liberty. The tallest turbines are almost as tall as the Eiffel Tower. In the future, each wind turbine will be able to supply a midsize town with all its energy needs.

Modern wind turbines are an engineering marvel. The wind spins two or three giant blades built from fiberglass-reinforced polyester or epoxy. Engineers link the blades to an internal shaft that rotates between 30 and 60 revolutions per minute. The shaft connects to a gearbox that increases the rotations to 1,000 to 1,800 rpm. The gearbox connects to a generator that converts this rapid rotation into electricity. Modern turbines consist of over 8,000 parts. Engineers are constantly working to make these parts more efficient to convert a higher portion of the wind's energy into electricity.

The wind energy industry is booming in the USA. Forty-three states have over 500 wind-related manufacturing facilities, and all fifty states utilize wind power. The United States wind industry currently employs more than 114,000 people. According to the Bureau of Labor Statistics, a wind-turbine technician is the most rapidly growing occupation in the USA. The wind energy industry also employs engineers, mechanics, installers, energy auditors, and other jobs.

The USA increased its wind capacity from 4.2 gigawatts (GW) in 2000 to over 135 GW by 2021. Texas, Oklahoma, and Iowa are the biggest producers of onshore wind power. These states are in the wind corridor that spans from Texas to Wyoming. The USA has even more potential for offshore wind turbines.

Offshore winds are more consistent and powerful than overland winds. The Biden administration recently declared its desire to have the USA generate over 30 GW of electricity from offshore wind energy by 2030. That is enough electricity to power more than ten million homes. McKinsey Consulting Firm estimates that we can increase the world production of offshore wind power to 630 GW by 2050, or enough to power over 470 million homes.

Wind energy has several advantages. It is clean, inexhaustible, and inexpensive. Unlike solar energy, the wind can blow all day and night. Winds usually blow in the cold and warm seasons.

However, wind capacity varies by region. In the USA, winds are strongest between North Texas to North Dakota. This region is called the wind corridor. In Europe, the wind is ferocious along the Atlantic Coast. Portugal, Ireland, the UK, Belgium, the Netherlands, and the Nordic countries have impressive capacities for wind power.

Mediterranean Europe and Central Europe are far less windy. In China, the wind blows stronger in the northeast and the west.

Power companies often lease land from farmers to install wind turbines. Leasing land for wind provides additional income to landowners in rural areas. Landowners typically get $4,000 to $8,000 per year for each turbine. According to the American Wind Energy Association, wind-turbine lease payments add up to around $250 million. Leasing land for wind energy provides needed income for economically troubled rural areas.

Offshore wind turbines make wind power available to more regions. Since there are no obstructions over water, offshore winds are more consistent and forceful. The Eastern Seaboard and the Midwest regions have an abundance of wind blowing near the shore of the Gulf of Mexico, the Atlantic Ocean, and the Great Lakes. Offshore turbines are pricier and more complicated to install, but they are typically larger and produce more energy than their onshore cousins.

Nonetheless, wind power does have a couple of drawbacks. Wind turbines are loud; turbines create both mechanical noise from the engine and noise from the blades as they cut through the air. These noises can be disruptive to people and animals. Turbines harm nature in other ways. In Hawaii, for instance, wind turbines have injured and killed several native species of birds and the endangered ʻōpeʻapeʻa (the Hawaiian Hoary Bat).

It is more economical to build multiple turbines in the same area since they can all connect to the same grid. Power companies must seek large windy areas far from people to build wind farms. By contrast, we can place solar panels almost anywhere. The sustainable economy of the future is likely to rely on solar power as its primary source and wind power as an important secondary source of energy.

Dammed if We Do

There are other sources of renewable energy besides solar and wind power. Until recently, the most important renewable energy was hydroelectricity. Engineers create hydroelectricity by building a dam in a river. The water accumulates behind the dam creating a reservoir. Then, the plant operator releases the water through a pipe known as a penstock into a room with generators. The rapidly moving water causes the generators to spin and produce electricity.

In 2020, hydroelectricity generated 7.3% of the electricity in the USA and 37% of the electricity from renewable sources. Dams generate substantial electricity and water. The most powerful dam in the USA is the Grand Coulee Dam, located on the Columbia River in Washington State. It contains 9 million cubic meters of concrete and supplies 6.8 GW of electricity to households in eight states. The Hoover Dam, located on the border of Utah and Arizona, creates Lake Mead, which supplies water to over 25 million people in seven states. Dams often create lakes for recreation. For instance, the Bagnell Dam in Missouri created the Lake of the Ozarks, which stretches for 92 miles and provides many recreation opportunities.

The USA was the leading producer of hydroelectricity for decades, but recently China took over the reins by building the world's largest dam. The Three Gorges Dam on the Yangtze River dwarfs all others. It is 7,660 feet long and has a maximum height of 607 feet. It is made from 28 million cubic meters of concrete and has thirty-two turbines that generate 22.5 GW of electricity, enough to power millions of Chinese.

Dams, unfortunately, create steep environmental and social costs. The Three Gorges Dam, which cost $24 billion to build, created a large reservoir that displaced over 1.2 million people. That reservoir also threatens many plants and animals in an area that accounts for 20% of Chinese plants and multiple animals, including the giant panda. Additionally, the rising water pressure creates floods and landslides.

Throughout the world, dams flood areas, kill plants, disrupt animal migrations, and, sometimes, displace people. Some prevent fish like salmon from migrating upriver to spawn. They also block rich soil from floating downstream. Their construction and water use reduce water flows and can devastate communities downstream. The

Hoover Dam, for instance, depleted the Colorado River so much that it dries up completely before reaching the Gulf of California.

In 1950, dams produced 30% of the electricity in the USA, and the country kept building more of them. However, since 2012, US states have dismantled over 1,700 dams out of environmental concerns. The largest dam removal in history will take place in 2024. California plans to demolish the Klamath River Dam, which prevents the once abundant Chinook salmon from migrating upstream to spawn, diverts water from farms downstream, and alters the region's ecosystem.

Hydroelectricity served a pivotal role in the past. However, the USA and other countries are realizing its negative environmental impacts and are reducing their hydroelectricity capacity. While developing countries like China and Brazil will continue to use hydroelectricity, it will likely diminish in importance in highly developed countries.

One Man's Trash

Solar energy, wind power, and hydroelectricity are the most common renewable energies. However, there are several other methods. One approach is to extract energy from our trash. Our garbage contains chemical energy, which typically goes to waste (pun intended). We can convert solid waste into energy using pyrolysis, gasification, or decomposition. These methods help us produce energy and manage our waste by turning our trash into treasure.

A lot of our garbage contains carbon. Scientists developed a method called pyrolysis to convert plastics and organic materials, which are carbon-based, into fuels. Pyrolysis involves heating biomass to between 800 and 900 Fahrenheit in an oxygen-deprived chamber. The process breaks materials into solid char, liquid bio-oil, and synthetic gas. We can use bio-oil to create biodiesel to power vehicles and machines. Synthetic gas contains hydrogen, methane, carbon monoxide, carbon dioxide, other hydrocarbons, and water vapor. It is often burned in a furnace to create the heat needed for pyrolysis.

Gasification entails heating organic materials between 1,400 and 1,700 Fahrenheit inside incinerators while injecting oxygen. The process produces carbon monoxide and hydrogen-rich gas. Suppliers can use this gas as fuel in diesel engines, for heating, and to generate electricity in gas turbines.

Organic material in landfills releases methane under anaerobic (without oxygen) decomposition by bacteria. Landfills release around 15.1% of human-produced methane in the USA, or about the greenhouse gas emissions of 21.6 million vehicles. However, some local governments trap the methane and burn it in gas generators to produce heat or electricity. The process has two benefits. It reduces the amount of methane that landfills release and using methane to produce electricity reduces our dependence on coal.

Sweden sends less than 1% of its municipal waste to landfills. The Swedish government recycles about half of the country's solid waste. It then incinerates any remaining carbon-based waste and converts it to bio-oil. The incinerators generate one ton of oil for every three tons of municipal waste. Sweden is so efficient at converting garbage into fuel that it imports solid waste from Norway, Italy, the UK, and other countries. While the process releases some greenhouse gases, it is considerably cleaner than burning fossil fuels and helps regions get rid of unsightly garbage.

Great Bowels of Fire

Humans can also generate renewable energy from the heat beneath the earth's surface. We can produce geothermal energy in regions with volcanic activity. Companies generate geothermal power by drilling deep wells that reach a heated underground reservoir. There are three methods to create electricity from boiling water.

1. The dry steam method allows steaming water to rise to the surface and drive turbines.
2. The flash method injects cold water down a well into a hotspot below the earth. The water heats up, reaches the surface as steam, and generates electricity by driving

turbines. Then the water is cooled and injected back into the well.

3. Finally, the binary method transfers the heat from the rising water into another liquid with a low boiling point. That liquid is converted into steam and used to drive turbines.

About twenty countries use geothermal energy, and the US produces the most. Nonetheless, it only represents 0.4% of its total energy production. California, which has the largest geothermal plant in the world, is responsible for 70.5% of geothermal energy production in the US. Nevada produces 10.2% of its electricity from geothermal energy, more than any other state.

Indonesia, the Philippines, and New Zealand—located along the Ring of Fire—also produce a fair amount of geothermal power. The Ring of Fire is an area of frequent volcanic activities that encircles the Pacific tectonic plate. No country, however, relies on geothermal energy as much as Iceland. The island nation is situated on the Mid-Atlantic Ridge and has multiple volcanoes. Iceland generates over 99.9% of its electricity from renewable energy, and 65% of its electricity comes from geothermal power. In addition to using geothermal energy to generate electricity, the Icelandic government pipes heated water underneath houses and commercial buildings to keep them warm during the chilling winters.

Geothermal energy is paramount to some countries like Iceland and New Zealand. However, its use is limited to regions with volcanic activity, and its worldwide capacity is small.

Geothermal energy has several challenges. Drilling in volcanic sites can release hydrogen sulfide, which smells like rotten eggs and causes skin irritations, headaches, and sleeping disorders. Building a plant in an area with volcanic activities is dangerous. Furthermore, the site may eventually cool down and become unproductive.

The New Wave
Other renewable energies represent a tiny part of our energy profile. We can also produce electricity from waves, tides, or nuclear fusion.

Wave energy and tidal energy only work in specific regions near a shore and have limited capacity. Nuclear fusion is a potentially promising technology. However, it is currently an unproven concept. While we can continue exploring other forms of energy since they work in some regions, our focus should remain on building up our solar and wind capacities.

Ocean waves can carry energy for thousands of miles until they crash near the shore. There are several ways to capture their energy. Power companies can anchor point absorber buoys to the ocean floor. Waves cause the buoys to undulate, leading a pump beneath each buoy to compress seawater into a turbine inside the buoy. Then, underwater cables transmit the electricity from the buoys to the shore.

Surface attenuators also capture the waves' kinetic energy. Attenuators consist of multiple pipes and look like giant sea snakes. The joints between pipes have hydraulic pumps that drive a generator. As with point absorber buoys, underwater cables carry the electricity ashore. Overtopping devices have a similar structure to point absorber buoys. However, instead of the waves pushing a buoy, their crests flow over the device into a reservoir. The water propels a turbine as it drains from the device. As with other forms of wave energy, underwater cables carry the electricity to the shore.

The final way to capture wave energy is by using a turbine house. This structure captures the waves' energy as they reach the shore. A tapered channel with converging walls compresses waves into a small space intensifying their energy. The surging water propels air into a turbine. The turbines spin and create electricity in the process. Finally, the water flows out through a separate pipe, allowing the next wave to enter.

Wave energy does not create pollution. Moreover, these technologies are safe for humans, and we can use them on a small or large scale. However, while we have effective ways to harvest energy from waves, wave energy has multiple drawbacks. For starters, they only work in regions with large, consistent waves. Additionally, connecting buoys, attenuators, or overtopping devices to the shore with cables is expensive. The equipment can disrupt sea life or get damaged during storms. A few countries, such as Australia and Portugal, utilize wave energy, but its use is limited and unlikely to grow substantially.

We can also harness the power of tides to generate electricity. Tides are the daily rising and falling of the sea due to the gravitational pulls of the sun and moon. Engineers can convert the kinetic energy from the tides by building a barrage that forces water to speed through a turbine or by placing tidal turbines in the water. Tidal energy is clean, efficient, and consistent. The tides in the ocean rise and fall with such consistency that we can predict their occurrence years in advance.

Despite its advantages, we scarcely utilize tidal energy. While every ocean and sea experiences tides, we can only use tidal energy in specific locations where the difference between low and high tides is substantial. The equipment used to generate tidal energy is expensive to build, install, and maintain. Furthermore, structures like barrages are disruptive to people and wildlife. Therefore, tidal energy is unlikely to play a significant role in our future.

Nuclear fusion merges two light nuclei into a heavier element. During the fusion, some of the mass becomes energy. All visible stars, including our sun, generate nuclear fusion in their core. Theoretically, we could fuse two hydrogen isotopes into helium on earth. The reaction will release neutrons and ample energy. To achieve fusion, scientists must collide isotopes under extreme temperatures and heat. The temperature in the accelerator must exceed 100 million degrees Celsius. While there are a couple operating fusion reactors, the concept is still largely theoretical. It could be a long time before nuclear fusion supports humanity's needs.

There are many ways to produce renewable energy. However, the primary sources of electricity in the future should be solar and wind energy. Other renewable energies only work well in certain regions. In a sustainable economy, we can have a rich energy profile with power companies using various types of sustainable energy connected to smart electric grids.

CHAPTER 10: STORING SUSTAINABLE ENERGY

Even if you're on the right track, you'll get run over if you just sit there. Will Rogers

Sunny is hardly the first word that comes to mind when people describe Germany. The winters in Germany are dark and cold, and even the summers are often cool and cloudy. Visitors to Europe do not travel to Germany to bask in the sun. Nonetheless, Germany leads Europe in solar and wind power production thanks to its aggressive subsidies. However, Germany's dependence on renewable energy creates an interesting dilemma. Germany produces too much energy on sunny and windy summer days and not enough during winter or windless nights.

When Germany generates a surplus of energy, it exports it to its neighbors, Austria, the Netherlands, Switzerland, and France. When Germany needs more electricity, it imports it from its neighbors. Ironically, Germany's neighbors benefit from its investment in renewable energy more than it does. In 2012, electricity cost $352 a megawatt-hour in Germany but only $238 in the Netherlands, $222 in Switzerland, and $187 in France. Germany could solve this inequity by storing the excess electricity that it creates. Switzerland, for instance, stores some of the inexpensive electricity it purchases from Germany using pumped hydro and compressed air technologies. This chapter describes various methods to store renewable energy and explains why large-scale energy storage is essential for a sustainable energy economy.

Storing for a Rainy Day

There is enough energy from the sun, the wind, and other renewable sources to supply all of our energy needs many times over. However, most renewable energy is intermittent and inconsistent. The sun does not shine at night, the wind is not always blowing, and waves near the shore are not always large enough to propel turbines. Moreover, there are large fluctuations between the solar energy available in the summer and winter. Therefore, we need ways to store renewable energy when we generate a lot of it so that we can use it when we do not generate enough.

We must store solar and wind energy when we generate excess supply to use when we have excess demand. We can preserve energy for toys, electronics, and cars in batteries. However, storing energy for cities and regions requires large-scale storage solutions. Governments must help societies shift to sustainable energy by investing in ways to store massive quantities of energy.

Energy is either potential or kinetic. Potential energy resides in an object based on its position, chemical composition, magnetism, or internal stress. Kinetic energy is the energy that an object possesses by being in motion. When you stand and hold a ball, that ball has potential energy. If you drop the ball, its energy becomes kinetic. Potential energy includes chemical energy, mechanical energy (such as a stretched spring), gravitational energy, and nuclear energy. Kinetic energy consists of electromagnetic radiation (such as light), thermal energy, motion energy, and electricity.

The ability to convert energy from one form to another aided the development of the human race. Prehistoric humans learned how to convert the chemical energy in wood into a fire that provided heat and light. The industrial revolution was possible because we learned how to convert the chemical energy in coal and oil into heat and electricity. Engineers used heat to produce steam that caused machine parts to move. Humans also used steam to force turbines to spin through magnetic fields in generators and produce electricity.

We can use electricity in many ways. We can use it to light our homes, operate machines, and charge vehicles. However, we cannot store it. Storing electricity requires converting it into potential energy. For example, we can use electricity to charge rechargeable batteries with chemical energy. Batteries are effective on a small scale. However, to use renewable energy, we must develop ways to store massive amounts of energy.

The Shape of Water

One of the oldest ways to store large quantities of energy is using pumped hydro storage facilities. These facilities have a lower and an upper reservoir connected by a pipe called a penstock. When power companies generate excess energy, it pumps water from the lower to the upper reservoir. When the company experiences excess demand for electricity, the facility releases water down the penstock. Like other hydroelectricity facilities, water flows through turbines and generates electricity. The energy needed to pump water uphill is 15% to 30% higher than the energy produced when the water is released. Thus, these facilities experience a net energy loss but still provide an effective way to store energy.

The USA built several pumped hydro storage facilities between 1960 and 1990 to balance surges in supply and demand for electricity. Several countries have shown a renewed interest in these facilities to store energy from renewable sources. Pumped storage facilities can pump water to the upper reservoir when the sun or wind creates excess energy. The facility releases the water to generate electricity in the evenings or on windless days. Pumped hydro can also help balance energy demand between the summer and winter.

Pumped hydro storage is the most common way of storing energy, but it has shortcomings. First, it necessitates a sizable capital investment. A facility costs between $1.3 and $3.3 billion. Secondly, it requires a specific topography. The technology needs locations with a height differential and enough space to build two reservoirs. The reservoirs flood areas and potentially disrupt local ecosystems. The fluctuations in the water level between energy storage and energy production can be disruptive to wildlife. While pumped hydro storage is likely to play a significant role in energy storage, it is only a part of the solution.

Under Pressure

We can also store energy by compressing air or other gases. Humans have been using compressed air since the 1870s, but employing this method for large-scale storage is a novel concept. Currently, we utilize two ways to compress air, Compressed Air Energy Storage (CAES) and Liquid Air Energy Storage (LAES).

Germany built the first CAES in 1978. CAES systems pump compressed air or other gases into a cavern during energy surpluses and release it during energy shortages. Facilities pump cooled, compressed air deep underground. They store air under 1,100 pounds per square inch of pressure. The pressure is roughly seventy-five times the pressure on the earth's surface. When there is excess demand for energy, the facility releases the air from the cavern. The expanding air then spins turbines at the surface and produces electricity.

CAES can use existing structures such as defunct salt caverns or abandoned mines. Therefore, they have a relatively low installation cost. CAES facilities also have a relatively short start-up time and can provide electricity in as little as nine minutes during emergencies. Furthermore, since compressed air is stored underground, CAES facilities require little space and do not burden the local ecosystem. The company Hydostor built two CAES facilities that store 10-gigawatt of energy and release 12 hours of electricity to the power grid.

The biggest drawback of CAES is its reliance on topography. To be cost-effective, CAES facilities must use existing caverns. These caverns must be airtight. Relying on existing caverns means that the CAES facility might be far from the population center that it serves. Our capacity to store energy as compressed air depends on the availability of viable sites.

An alternative to CAES systems is LAES or Liquid Air Energy Storage. It is a newer technology. England built the first commercial LAES in 2020. A LAES facility uses electricity during periods of excess supply to cool air or nitrogen into liquid. Then, the facility stores liquefied air or nitrogen in airtight tanks. When there is excess demand for electricity, the liquid is evaporated and heated. This process produces a high-pressure gas, which the LAES facility uses to drive turbines and produce electricity.

LAES is a relatively new technology, but it has great promise. The primary advantage of LAES facilities over CAES facilities is that we can build them almost anywhere. Power companies can construct LAES facilities next to LNG terminals and use the cold waste from the LNG plant for cooling. LAES plants can produce hundreds of megawatts of output. They provide a great way to store energy without using much space.

In 2012, Vermont approved a plan to get 90% of its power from renewable energy by 2050. Vermont contracted a British company called Highview Power to build LAES facilities. One LAES facility can provide power to around 50,000 homes for eight hours. Energy storage can also help states manage fluctuations in demand. Some of Vermont's towns experience congestion in their electric transmission lines, and LAES facilities near these towns can release energy when the transmission lines are overburdened.

The Heat is On

Power companies can store energy as cold, compressed gas. They can also do the opposite and store energy using a hot liquid. We can achieve Thermal Energy Storage (TES) using a one-tank or a two-tank system. A two-tank system has one tank with cold and another with hot water. The facility uses excess renewable energy to heat one of the tanks. When there is excess demand for electricity, the hot liquid flows into a heat exchanger and boils water. The resulting steam causes turbines to spin. Then, the liquid cools down and returns to the cold tank. We already use two-tank systems to store energy from Concentrated Solar Power plants. However, we can use it to store energy from other sources too.

A single-tank thermocline system stores thermal energy in a medium such as silica sand. The bottom of the tank contains a colder, denser medium, while the top consists of a warmer state of the same material. Since the hotter material is less dense, it flows to the top of the tank creating a stratification line, known as a thermocline, between the hot and the cold parts. The plant uses a heat transfer fluid to heat the top of the tank and move the thermocline down, thus increasing the amount of energy. When the facility needs to create electricity, it uses heat from the tank to warm fluid into steam. The stream flows through a turbine and generates electricity.

Daytona State College uses a TES system to help cool down its buildings. The college, located in the warm state of Florida, siphons hot water from the top of the tank at night, when electricity is cheap, chills them, and returns them to the bottom of the tank. During the daytime, the college uses cold water from the tank's bottom to help cool the building on its campus. The system saves Daytona State College about $200,000 a year.

TES systems are eco-friendly and do not require much space. However, they need a substantial investment. They could play a significant role in a sustainable energy economy along with other methods of storing energy.

Spinning the Wheel

The systems discussed so far can store a lot of energy. However, power companies usually have to build them in specific locations. Additionally, it takes them time to release energy. We also need ways to store and release energy quickly inside cities to balance short-term fluctuations in energy demand.

Flywheels and sustainable fuel storage can store energy near consumers and release it rapidly. Flywheels are rotating mechanical devices inside airtight chambers in near-vacuum conditions. Unlike other energy storage facilities, they use kinetic, not potential, energy. We can use electricity to make flywheels rotate during periods of excess supply and then convert their kinetic energy back into electricity when needed.

Beacon Power built a 20-megawatt FES plant in Hazel Township, Pennsylvania. The plant converts up to 97% of the flywheels' kinetic energy into electricity. Moreover, it can generate electricity in just four seconds and swiftly respond to demand surges.

FES facilities have several advantages. FES systems do not create emissions and pose no threat to the local ecosystems. FES facilities are safe, and we can construct them inside cities. Since FES facilities are usually close to the populations they serve, they deliver electricity more efficiently and faster than other energy storage systems.

However, they have a couple of disadvantages. Unlike pumped storage hydropower or compressed air storage, FES systems cannot store electricity for long. Eventually, the wheels slow down. Another disadvantage is that flywheels have limited capacity, whereas other energy storage facilities can store large amounts of energy. Finally, FES systems require frequent maintenance to keep the flywheel as frictionless as possible.

Nonetheless, we can use FES systems to store energy locally. The fact that they need little space and can release energy quickly make them ideal to utilize in cities and towns to balance short-term surges and ebbs in energy demand. We should use FES systems together with other energy storage systems.

Hydro Planning

We can also store energy as a sustainable fuel. We can use hydrogen to store and transport energy from renewable resources. Power companies can use sustainable electricity to separate water into hydrogen and oxygen with electrolysis. They can then store the hydrogen as a liquid by cooling it to -252.8° Celsius (-421°F).

Power companies can combine hydrogen with oxygen inside a solid oxide fuel cell (SOFC) to generate electricity. SOFCs operate in high temperatures of 1,500 to 1,800 Fahrenheit. While they are expensive to build, they are efficient and can convert massive energy. Presently they convert up to 60% of the energy from liquid hydrogen to electricity. If we learn how to trap and use their heat, they will convert 80% of the fuel into electricity.

We can also store energy as biofuel. There are different biofuels, including ethanol, biodiesel, and algal oil. As explained previously, we must use land, fertilizers, pesticides, and water to develop most biofuels. However, algal biofuel does not have most of these drawbacks, and we might be able to use it to store energy in the future.

Since wind and solar energy—the primary sources of renewable energy—are intermittent, shifting to sustainable energy necessitates storing energy on a large scale. We can preserve energy as pumped water, compressed air, hot gases, or hydrogen fuel. Fortune Business Insight, a consulting firm, predicts that the energy storage industry will grow from $9.1 billion in 2021 to over $30 billion at the end of the decade.

Eventually, we will likely use a combination of different storage technologies. We will probably use pumped hydropower and compressed air storage for long-term energy storage while utilizing flywheels and sustainable fuels to store energy locally and balance short-term fluctuations.

As noted at the beginning of the chapter, building our energy storage capacity would help countries utilize renewable energy. Germany has large energy surpluses in the summer and sizable deficits in the winter. Energy storage will allow Germany and other countries to rely on renewable energy by storing it when they have too much and releasing it when they do not have enough. It will also help stabilize energy prices by matching the demand and supply of electricity.

CHAPTER 11: GOING NUCLEAR

Nuclear power is one hell of a way to boil water.
Albert Einstein

On March 11, 2011, Japan experienced its strongest recorded earthquake. The Tōhoku earthquake occurred 81 miles away from the shore of northeast Japan and created a tsunami that raced toward the Japanese shoreline. The tsunami arrived 10 minutes later as a mountain of water. It flooded Japanese towns, crushing everything in its path. The floods killed over 17,000 people, destroyed a million buildings, and caused over $235 billion in damages. The water breached the seawalls of the Fukushima Daiichi Nuclear Power Plant, flooded its emergency generator, and caused a meltdown in the plant's nuclear core. The incident was a level seven nuclear disaster, the highest level.

The Fukushima incident caused worldwide concerns about nuclear power. However, not a single person died from exposure to radiation in Fukushima. A study conducted ten years after the disaster found no increase in cancer in Japan. Following the meltdown, the government hurriedly evacuated over 300,000 people from the area. Many evacuees died from fatigue or illnesses since local hospitals shut down. Japan's Reconstruction Agency estimated that over 1,300 people perished during the evacuation, more than the number of people who died in the Chornobyl nuclear disaster and all other nuclear disasters combined. Historically, more people died because of fear of nuclear disasters than from radiation. This chapter explores how nuclear fission works and why we should use more of it.

Splitting Atoms

Energy is either renewable or non-renewable. Most renewable energy, including solar, wind, and wave energy, is sustainable, which means that it is long-lasting and eco-friendly. Most non-renewable energy, such as coal and petroleum, is finite and harmful to humans and the environment. Nuclear power, however, is non-renewable and sustainable. Since nuclear material decays slowly, we can use it for centuries. Unlike fossil fuels, nuclear power does not create emissions. By managing nuclear waste, we can use nuclear energy with little environmental harm. We should use more nuclear power alongside renewable energy.

Humans generate nuclear power by breaking enriched uranium into lighter elements. A chain reaction begins by bombarding uranium with neutrons. The neutrons cause the uranium to break, creating lighter elements, intense gamma radiation, and more neutrons. This process, called nuclear fission, releases a lot of energy. Fission takes place in the reactor core. The core consists of fuel elements (enriched uranium) and control rods submerged in water. The water slows down the neutrons in the reaction. The control rods consist of boron or cadmium that can absorb the neutrons and stop the reaction.

The radiation from nuclear fission creates a lot of heat. Power companies use this heat to turn water into steam that they channel into turbines. The turbines connect to a generator that converts their kinetic energy into electricity.

The USA did not initially develop nuclear fission to generate electricity. Americans invented the process to build lethal bombs. In 1939, President Franklin D. Roosevelt organized a group of scientists and military personnel to study uranium. In 1942, he authorized the formation of the Manhattan Project to develop nuclear bombs. USA intelligence operatives reported to the President that Nazi Germany was building a nuclear weapon, and he decided that the US must create it first to win the war. After testing in New Mexico, the project successfully developed several bombs.

On July 26, 1945, the USA delivered an ultimatum to Japan—surrender under an outlined set of terms or face a "prompt and utter destruction." When Japan did not give in, a US plane dropped a bomb dubbed Little Boy over Hiroshima on August 6, killing over 80,000 people. Three days later, the US dropped another bomb on Nagasaki, killing 40,000 more. These bombs completely evaporated people and leveled large sections of each city. Thousands more died from radiation-induced cancer afterward.

After World War II, the Soviet Union developed nuclear weapons leading to the Cold War. The Cold War was a period of political and military tension between the West and the Soviet Union, from 1947 until 1991. Both sides learned how to use nuclear energy for other purposes, such as nuclear submarines. In the 1950s, the USA and the Soviet Union built nuclear plants to produce electricity.

Nuclear power is inexpensive. Until 2010, producing electricity from nuclear power was cheaper than oil, natural gas, or renewable energy. It costed about the same as coal. Recently, explorations for natural gas and the development of renewable energy made them less expensive than nuclear power. It is likely that if we invest in nuclear energy, we can reduce its cost too. It is an abundant source of energy. The Nuclear Energy Agency (NEA) believes that our reactors could run for over 200 years, given our known uranium reserves. If we continue to search for nuclear material, we are likely to find additional reserves.

Nuclear Reactions

A 2019 Gallup poll found that Americans disagree over the use of nuclear power. 49% of Americans favor using nuclear power, while 49% oppose it. Similarly, 47% of Americans believe nuclear plants are safe compared to 49% who consider them unsafe.

There are four common concerns regarding nuclear energy: First, nuclear plants can experience meltdowns and spread radiation that harms nearby communities. Second, working in nuclear plants might be unsafe. Third, terrorists can convert radioactive material into weapons. Finally, nuclear power creates radioactive waste, which countries must manage.

Nuclear meltdowns are extremely rare, but they were more common in the early days of atomic power. In the 1950s, several nuclear incidents exposed workers to radiation, which caused them to develop cancer. Since 1961, humanity has seen three significant incidents, and only one had casualties. Modern safety protocols make exposure to nuclear radiation in highly-developed countries like the United States highly improbable.

In 1978, there was a meltdown in the Three Mile Island Power Station in Pennsylvania. Not a single person died from the incident. There were also no detectable health effects for the workers or nearby residents. The radiation released from the incident was lower than a single X-ray shot. Yet, the political reaction to the incident was so strong that the United States canceled over 120 nuclear reactor orders and halted the construction of generators for nearly thirty years.

The worst nuclear disaster in history was in Chornobyl, Ukraine, a satellite of the Soviet Union at the time. The 1986 meltdown at Chornobyl killed twenty-eight individuals and led to a massive evacuation of over 300,000 people from the area. Following the incident, thousands more died from radiation during the explosion or the cleanup. The region is still a ghost town and an attraction for curious tourists.

Chornobyl was the only nuclear meltdown since the 1960s that killed people. Ukraine was a part of the Soviet Union at the time of the incident, and the USSR had a horrific safety record. The Soviet Union did not place the same value on human life that countries do today. A nuclear disaster like Chornobyl is unlikely in the USA or Western Europe, where nuclear power is carefully monitored and regulated.

Despite the many meltdowns on the Simpsons, working in nuclear plants is safe. In fact, nuclear energy is the safest source of energy. It is safer than fossil fuels, hydroelectricity, wind power, or solar energy. More employees die from installing wind turbines or solar panels than from producing nuclear energy.

Modern wind turbines are less safe than nuclear plants. They weigh hundreds of tons and exceed 300 feet in height. Firms assemble them in giant plants with heavy machinery and transport them using large trucks. To ensure the turbine can stand upright, the company must lay steel foundations that weigh hundreds of tons into the ground. Then, a giant crane hoists sections of the turbine and assembles them on top of each other. Each of the turbine's rings can weigh over 100 tons. A crew suspended on a platform fits each part of the turbine into the part below it. Any misstep can crush a crewmember.

The construction and installation of solar panels are also hazardous. Companies produce solar panels in factories with multiple machines in a sterile environment. Factory workers risk mechanical injuries. People often install solar panels on rooftops high above the ground, and installers risk falling during installation. Working in solar and wind energy industries is relatively safe, but working in a nuclear plant is safer.

Coal is responsible for 100,000 deaths, hydroelectricity for 1,400 deaths, rooftop solar for 440 deaths, and wind energy for 150 deaths per terawatt hour. By comparison, nuclear power led to 90 deaths per terawatt hour. Nuclear energy has the lowest mortality rate of any energy source. It is the safest way to produce electricity, and we should use it more.

Another concern is that terrorists can convert nuclear material into weapons. After all, the US first developed fission to produce bombs. The threat of a nuclear attack was also a concern during the Cold War. Building radioactive weapons requires enriching uranium, a complex process that requires scientific knowledge and considerable resources. Seventy-five years after the Hiroshima bombing, only nine countries developed such weapons. Terrorists will probably never have the capacity to build nuclear weapons. However, we must keep nuclear waste secured to prevent terrorists from using it to create a dirty bomb, a conventional bomb laced with radioactive waste.

Radioactive, Radioactive

While nuclear power is safe, we must figure out what to do with the radioactive waste that the process produces. It takes thousands of years for spent nuclear fuel to decay completely. Radioactive waste can cause cancer and pollute water supplies. However, our anxiety

118

about radioactive waste might be unjustified. We have no documented cases of anyone dying from radiation caused by spent fuel.

In the USA, plants store nuclear waste in pools inside or near the plant. Since the spent fuel emits radiation, the plant must chill the water in the pool. All nuclear plants have backup generators that keep the water in the reservoirs cold if the power fails. After ten to twenty years, the material decays to a point where it is relatively safe to store in casks. There is no permanent storage site for nuclear waste in the United States. Instead, power companies ship radioactive waste to one of over seventy temporary storage sites in thirty-four states. To date, there have not been any radiological leaks from these sites.

There is, of course, a probability that stored nuclear waste can leak in the future. However, even if that happens, it would still be statistically the safest form of energy. When it comes to nuclear energy, people often ignore facts. In a brilliant book titled *Factfullness,* Swedish physician Hans Rosling writes about how we fear nuclear power because we fear things we do not understand. The probability of dying from radiation is minuscule. However, the media plays on our fears. For instance, the media released numerous stories about the nuclear meltdown following the tsunami in Fukushima. Yet, it mostly ignored the thousands who died from the terrifying floods or the rushed evacuation.

As safe as nuclear energy is, we can make it even safer. Over 90% of the nuclear waste can be reprocessed and used to produce more electricity. France ships most of its spent fuel to a facility in the Netherlands, where it is cooled for three years, mixed with oxide fuel, and returned to France for reuse. The USA does not currently reprocess radioactive waste, but France, Japan, and other countries do. If the US reprocessed its spent fuel, it would have far less radioactive waste to store.

We can also better manage radioactive waste by creating a secure nuclear repository. Congress proposed using Yucca Mountain in Nevada as a national nuclear repository. The plan was to store waste inside capsules within tunnels deep underground. The government built the Yucca Mountain Repository but never used it because of local opposition.

Finland opened the world's first long-term nuclear waste repository in Onkalo. It is 400 meters or over 1,200 feet deep. The area is sparsely populated, geographically stable, and never experienced earthquakes. Finland stores radioactive waste in rods, and stacks the rods in casks. It places these casks in nuclear-resistant capsules inside depository rooms sealed with water-resistant clay and cement. With so many layers of containment, the probability of any leak occurring is insignificant. Even in the unlikely case of a leak, it will take place deep underground.

A Tale of Two Countries

Countries can choose one of three paths. The first path is to let the market decide which energy we will use. Some economists argue that energy suppliers will automatically switch to renewable energies if their cost falls. This argument is misguided. Even though solar and wind energy are becoming cheaper, governments must invest in renewable infrastructure to encourage their use. After all, the USA and other countries helped build the infrastructure to transport and deliver fossil fuels by building pipelines, ports, trains, and roads.

We must discontinue using fossil fuels quickly because they harm the environment and create climatic instability. We do not have the luxury of waiting for the market to solve this problem. Finally, even though some renewable energies are cheaper than fossil fuels, gas and oil companies will lobby to continue their use since they control these resources.

The second path, supported by most environmentalists, is to switch from fossil fuels and nuclear power to renewable energies by subsidizing their production and taxing fossil fuels. While we should eventually generate most of our energy from renewable sources, it would take decades to build our renewable energy capacity and longer to construct the energy storage facilities we need. Most renewable energy is intermittent, and we need to generate some of our electricity from a consistent source. We must support renewable energy, but it is not enough.

The third path is to invest in renewable energy while simultaneously increasing our nuclear energy capacity. Doing so will help us eliminate our dependence on fossil fuels within decades. Furthermore, since nuclear fission works all the time, we would be less concerned about the fluctuations in the energy supply. Investing in nuclear power will diversify and secure our energy supply.

After Fukushima, Germany chose to stop using nuclear energy. Because it was not producing enough electricity from renewable energy in the winter, this decision caused Germany to backtrack and increase its reliance on coal, the dirtiest of all fossil fuels. France chose the third path. They invested heavily in nuclear power and almost stopped using fossil fuels for electricity. France generated over 75% of its electricity from nuclear power. France has the second-highest level of nuclear power per capita after Slovakia. Its reliance on nuclear energy means that France uses fewer fossil fuels. In 2015, France produced 7.5% of its electricity from fossil fuels compared to 55.6% in Germany.

France chose wisely. Nuclear power is abundant, efficient, and safe. If the US starts reprocessing spent fuel and approves a national repository, it can safely store radioactive waste. However, the government needs to ensure it transports radioactive waste safely. It should protect trains and trucks that transport radioactive waste from terrorist attacks.

By investing in renewable and nuclear energy, rapidly building our EV infrastructure, and developing carbon sinks like new forests, the USA could become carbon neutral by 2050. Western Europe is already on the path to carbon neutrality. China and India have pledged to become carbon neutral within fifty years. By the second half of the twenty-first century, the world could stop using fossil fuels to produce electricity. These goals are realistic, but we need to increase our nuclear energy capacity to achieve them.

SUMMARY OF PART III

We have various ways of generating electricity from renewable resources. Solar energy is abundant, clean, and can be installed anywhere. Thanks to recent advancements, it is the cheapest source of electricity. Wind turbines create noise and can harm aviary wildlife. Nonetheless, they are clean and can generate an impressive amount of inexpensive energy. Hydroelectricity is the most widely used renewable energy. Unfortunately, dams prevent wildlife migration, flood animal habitats, and may displace people.

Other technologies, such as wave, tidal, and geothermal, only work in specific regions and have other limitations. We should focus on increasing solar and wind energies. We should also build more nuclear power plants. While there are concerns about meltdowns and managing radioactive waste, nuclear power is safe, clean, and abundant. Additionally, we must develop ways to store large amounts of energy using various methods.

PART IV: MAKING SUSTAINABILITY STICK

Image by Joenomias found on https://pixabay.com

CHAPTER 12: SMOKESCREEN

For those who believe, no proof is necessary. For those who don't
believe, no proof is possible.
Stuart Chase.

In 1977, Philip Morris, R.J. Reynolds, and other tobacco giants met
to discuss protecting the industry's interests by promoting
controversy over smoking-related diseases and reassuring smokers.
They commissioned researchers to support the safety of cigarettes
and paid for advertisements in medical journals, which claimed that
the rise in lung cancer was due to pollution. They also broadcasted
testimonies by lifelong smokers about their outstanding health and
offered alternatives such as light cigarettes and filters. The
companies knew they were fighting a losing battle and that the
government would condemn tobacco, but they wanted to lose slowly.
It took the USA until 1990 to prohibit smoking on domestic flights
and more time to ban smoking in public buildings. Today, we know
that tobacco kills millions of people by causing cancer, respiratory
diseases, and heart attacks. Smokers, on average, live ten years less
than nonsmokers.

For decades, the gas and oil companies have utilized similar
tactics to the tobacco industry. They distorted data, confused the
public by claiming that global warming is a natural phenomenon,
and offered alternatives such as clean coal and natural gas.
Consequently, many people still do not understand that fossil fuels
are the leading cause of climate instability despite the
preponderance of scientific evidence. Few people understand the
magnitude of harm that fossil fuels cause. This chapter will elucidate
how the oil industry manipulates markets, lobbies governments for
subsidies, and hurts the sustainability movement through a clever
disinformation campaign.

It's All Uphill from Here

Scientists and writers have been predicting the demise of fossil fuels for decades. In 1956, geologist M. King Hubbard predicted that the US oil production would peak in 1970, and worldwide production would crest around 2000. We are now supposed to be experiencing a period of increasing oil scarcity and rapidly rising gas prices. If Hubbard had been right, countries would now be scrambling to find alternatives to petroleum. They are not.

Until recently, it looked like Hubbard was right. In 1970, USA petroleum production peaked at 9,637 per day, and by 2008 it fell to 5,000 barrels per day. Recently, however, the trend has reversed. By 2019, petroleum production in the US climbed to 12,248 barrels per day thanks to fracking and the discoveries of new reserves. Worldwide, proven oil reserves reached a trillion barrels in the 1990s and stopped growing. However, starting in 2002, we began discovering new reservoirs. By 2020, the known reserves of oil had reached 1.7 trillion barrels.

Hubbard based his prediction on sound scientific analysis. Nonetheless, he could not account for oil companies developing new ways to extract crude oil and natural gas. Fracking allowed the industry to siphon previously unreachable oil and natural gas from deep underground shales. Gas companies developed ways to drill deeper and extract difficult-to-reach oil and gas.

Hubbard accurately estimated how much oil was near the surface but could not predict how much oil existed well underground. Similarly, when the oil prices rose above $60 a barrel in the early 2000s, Canadian firms found it profitable to extract oil from tar sands, which is expensive since the firm must separate the oil and sand. Additionally, oil giants successfully lobbied governments to exploit naturally vulnerable areas, including rich fisheries and national parks.

There are currently no signs that our production of oil will fall soon. While oil and natural gas are finite resources, we cannot simply wait for their production to decline on its own. It will take decades before oil and gas production peaks and much longer before we stop using them. In the meantime, humanity will release a detrimental amount of greenhouse gases into the atmosphere, damage many ecosystems, and finance rogue nations like Russia and Venezuela. We must actively reduce our consumption of fossil fuels now by taxing them, regulating them, and subsidizing sustainable energy.

Powerful Players

One of the reasons it is difficult for sustainable energy producers to compete with fossil fuels is that OPEC and oil companies lobby for government support. The Organization of Petroleum Exporting Countries is an intergovernmental association of thirteen oil-producing countries. The organization aims to coordinate petroleum production to secure stable prices and reasonable profits.

OPEC produces about two-fifths of the world's oil and controls almost three-fifths of the proven reserves. Russia, which has the third-largest oil reserves, is not a member of OPEC but participates in OPEC+. OPEC+ includes ten additional countries with large oil reserves, which often collaborate with OPEC. OPEC+ influences oil prices by controlling a significant portion of its global supply.

OPEC seeks to stabilize oil prices by keeping them within a range. Low prices mean falling profits for its members. If oil prices drop too low due to falling demand, OPEC would typically cut oil production to prop them up. High prices can lead to political strife and incentivize countries to invest in alternative fuels. When oil prices rise too high due to a surge in demand or supply shocks, OPEC often boosts oil production to lower prices.

The US government is another powerful player that can influence oil prices. Following the OPEC crisis of 1974, the US developed large strategic petroleum reserves. These reserves are in four large caverns inside salt mines along the Gulf Coast. They can hold over 700 million barrels of petroleum. The US government can temporarily lower oil prices by releasing oil from these reserves.

The US and other countries also keep the price of oil low by subsidizing its production. According to the International Energy Agency, in 2018, the United States government spent $182 billion on oil subsidies and another $99 billion on subsidies for natural gas. Additionally, it allocated $143 billion to support electricity from fossil fuels. These subsidies keep the cost of fossil fuels artificially low and make it harder for alternative energies to compete.

On several occasions, the USA and OPEC were at odds about oil prices. When the US entered a recession in 2008, oil prices fell from $133 per barrel to under $40 per barrel. OPEC responded by cutting production by 2.2 million barrels a day. Their strategy was successful. By 2010, the oil price had climbed to over $80 per barrel. However, the USA pushed OPEC to keep the production of oil high. The federal government hoped low gasoline prices would help it recover from one of the worst recessions in history.

OPEC and the USA were at odds again at the beginning of 2022. President Biden aimed to release oil from the strategic reserves to stimulate the economy. OPEC believed this was unnecessary since gasoline prices, around three and a quarter dollars per gallon, were not historically high. It threatened to reduce oil production to counter any additional oil from the strategic reserves.

These oil poker games illustrate that the market alone does not determine oil prices. Players like OPEC and the United States influence oil prices. The USA and OPEC seem determined to keep oil prices stable. They manipulate prices to prevent them from falling too low or rising too high. It will take a long time before countries switch away from crude oil if we keep manipulating its price.

Grease Payments

Like OPEC, oil companies are also interested in ensuring that humanity continues to use oil. To help achieve this goal, oil companies lobby the US government for subsidies and concessions. The American Petroleum Institute, representing around 600 corporations that extract, refine, and distribute petroleum, is one of the most powerful lobbies in Washington. According to the House Committee on Oversight and Reform, the four largest oil producers and the API had spent $452.6 million since 2011 lobbying the federal government.

Lobbying surges during pivotal elections. In 2019 alone, the oil and gas industry spent $125.8 million lobbying policymakers, making it the fourth-largest lobby in the USA. The oil lobby finances congressional and presidential candidates in exchange for regulations that favor the industry. In addition to demanding subsidies, the oil industry lobbies the government for drilling rights, lax regulations, and low taxes.

Politicians need lobbying dollars to win elections, and many of them give the oil industry what it asks for to keep receiving funds. The oil industry has successfully lobbied the US government for subsidies, licenses to extract oil from national forests, low taxes on gasoline, and no carbon tax. For example, oil companies successfully lobbied to open over 1.5 million acres in the Arctic National Wildlife Refuge to drilling. The refuge, located in Alaska, is the largest in the USA. It is home to polar bears, caribou, Dall's sheep, and many other animals.

The oil lobby influences other national governments. Consequently, many countries subsidize fossil fuels even though they harm the environment. According to the International Energy Agency, national governments spent billions of dollars subsidizing fossil fuels. Governments dole out more to support fossil fuels than the Gross Domestic Product of most nations in the world. Moreover, subsidies for oil are on the rise. Petroleum subsidies increased by 80% between 2016 and 2018, while natural gas subsidies doubled.

Subsidies for fossil fuels, especially petroleum, are popular because they make energy more affordable. However, they also make it difficult to switch to sustainable energy because they keep fossil fuels artificially inexpensive. It is challenging for renewable energy suppliers to compete against an industry that receives billions in subsidies. Renewable energy suppliers are too small and decentralized to maintain an influential lobby. Even though it is currently less costly to produce electricity from solar panels or wind, the USA is likely to continue using fossil fuels for a long time because of favorable government subsidies and regulations.

Oil companies are not the only ones lobbying governments for concessions. Saudi Arabia spent over $100 million in the first decade of the twenty-first century lobbying the US government through domestic attorneys and companies. The Kingdom of Saudi Arabia is the largest global oil producer and has 16% of the world's proven reserves. Oil makes up 75% of Saudi's exports and 60% of its government revenue. With over 260 billion barrels of oil still in the ground, the Kingdom has a strong incentive to keep us pumping oil.

Smoke and Mirrors

In addition to gaining concessions from governments, the oil lobby also attempts to convince the public that climatic instability is not a significant concern. The industry has known about the effects of greenhouse gases for decades but always downplayed them. In 1980, Marty Hoffert, a physicist working for Exxon-Mobile, created a simulation that showed how the earth's surface temperature would increase if we kept spewing out greenhouse gases from fossil fuels. Hoffert presented his findings to the company's executives. His company refused to acknowledge his conclusions and countered that scientific evidence about global warming is inconclusive.

Hoffert had expected that his findings would lead to political actions. He explained, "We'll do the analyses, we'll write reports, the politicians of the world will see the reports, and they'll make the appropriate changes and transform our energy system somehow." He also noted, "I didn't realize how hard it would be to convince people, even when they saw objective evidence of this happening."

In 1988, the average temperature broke the record. By the early 1990s, the scientific community reached a consensus that human activities were causing the earth's temperature to rise. The oil lobby went on the offensive by commissioning research that cherry-picked data to demonstrate that global warming was not happening. For example, one paper pointed out that the temperature in Kentucky was getting colder even though other US states were getting warmer. They paid for articles claiming global warming was an unproven theory or that climate change was caused purely by natural phenomena. They paid politicians to scare the public about losing their jobs if we stopped using fossil fuels.

Convincing the public required a carefully orchestrated disinformation campaign. This disinformation campaign created fear, uncertainty, and doubt about climate change and renewable energy. The oil lobby posted articles to invoke skepticism about anthropogenic climate change. Some of these articles claimed that most warming was due to the earth coming out of the ice age. Other publications stated that the measurements taken by scientists were unreliable and that most of the apparent increase in temperature was due to heat generated by cities. Some stories labeled environmentalists and the liberal media as hysterical.

Just like the tobacco industry had misled people about the harms of smoking, the oil industry created uncertainty about climatic instability. Disinformation campaigns do not need to prove anything; they merely have to sow doubt and deflect people's attention from the real issue. For example, some climate change skeptics claim that the rise in global temperature is due to urban island heat. Cities generate heat from air conditioners, appliances, vehicles, and machines. Rooftops and asphalts also tend to trap heat. Indeed, cities are warmer, but that only explains a tiny fraction of the increase in global temperatures. Moreover, climatologists consistently measure temperatures far from cities. The urban heat islands effect cannot explain why temperatures rise at the poles or in the middle of the ocean thousands of miles away from cities.

Another claim the oil lobby created to sow doubt over global warming was that the earth is naturally warming because we are still recovering from the last glacial period. Similarly, some blogs claim that our planet is still warming up from the little ice age. The last glacial period ended 15,000 years ago. We are no longer recovering from it. The little ice age was not actually an ice age. It consisted of three brief periods of regional cooling in the 1650s, 1770s, and 1850s, which did not affect the global climate. Even

130

though these claims have no scientific merit, they provide ammunition for those who argue against anthropogenic (human-made) climate change.

The oil industry has succeeded in creating skepticism. Many people do not believe in the greenhouse effect despite ample evidence. The 1980s were, at the time, the hottest decade on record. Then the 1990s became the hottest decade, then the 2000s, and, most recently, the 2010s. According to the National Oceanic and Atmospheric Administration, the ten hottest years in recorded history have occurred since 2005. There were 103 named storms in 2020, tying the record set in 2018. The earth is losing roughly 13% of its Arctic ice each decade.

Due to climate instability, there are more frequent and intense storms, fires, droughts, floods, and heat waves. However, the disinformation campaign orchestrated by the oil industry is so effective that some people still do not think the world's climate is changing. Moreover, many who believe that our climate is changing attribute these changes to natural causes.

Perspectives are changing. A 2019 survey by Yale and George Mason universities revealed that 73% of Americans now believe global warming is happening, which is a 10% increase from 2015. Nonetheless, there is much work to be done. Climate skeptics are an influential political block in the USA, and we must continue to educate people about climate instability. To shift to a sustainable energy economy, we must combat the oil industry's disinformation campaign, convince people that climate instability exists, and push policymakers to make sustainability a priority. Hopefully, the smoke will clear soon, and everyone will see that climatic instability is happening and that we must eliminate fossil fuels to combat it.

CHAPTER 13: A PARTNERSHIP FOR THE PLANET

Those who cannot change their minds cannot change anything!
George Bernard Shaw

In 2019, a sixteen-year-old Swede named Greta Thunberg embarked on a sailing voyage from Plymouth, England. Her destination was the United Nations Headquarters in New York, where she delivered a speech on sustainability. She elected not to fly to the United States because airplanes emit greenhouse gases. Greta, who has Asperger's syndrome, became known worldwide when she left school for a year to advocate for environmental sustainability. Greta did not have a college degree or years of experience. However, she has an uncompromising spirit and a passion for the environment.

More people like Thunberg are advocating for sustainability. Many world leaders proclaim their commitment to sustainable energy, large automakers commit to producing more EVs, and investors rush to invest in EV companies. The shift to a sustainable energy economy seems inevitable, but it is not. Relying on sustainable energy requires profound changes in how consumers and voters think. Automakers must convince consumers to buy EVs, and voters must convince politicians to tax fossil fuels and support sustainable energy. This chapter describes how we can develop a global partnership for environmental sustainability.

Promises Broken, Promises Made

Managing climate change requires global cooperation among countries. World leaders first met to discuss our impact on the environment during the 1972 UN Conference on the Human Environment in Stockholm. Since then, world leaders have met multiple times to discuss global collaboration on environmental issues.

In 1987, the multinational commission authored a report called *Our Common Future.* They recognized that poverty in developing countries and overconsumption in developed countries strain the environment. Poor people must rely on marginal land and overuse natural resources such as forests. Overconsumption in developed countries results in pollution and garbage.

The report advocated for a future with moderate and sustainable consumption. It called for developed countries to support the economic development of poorer nations by canceling their debts and investing in sustainable development projects. It also urged governments to shift from fossil fuels to renewable energy.

The world met to discuss our common environmental future in Rio de Janeiro, Brazil, in 1992; in Kyoto, Japan in 1997; Johannesburg, South Africa in 2002; Rio again in 2012; and in Paris in 2015. Each conference produced new targets to reduce poverty, curtail the emissions of greenhouse gases, and invest in renewable energy.

These conferences had some success. For example, the 1997 Kyoto Protocol called for developed nations to reduce their emissions of five greenhouse gases to 5.2% lower than their 1990 levels by 2012. The USA agreed to the Kyoto Protocol. However, it did not ratify it and did not accomplish its goal. The other thirty-six signees eventually met their goals. Although, ten of them achieved them by buying carbon credits instead of reducing emissions. Several countries also reduced emissions by shifting some industrial production to developing countries.

In the past, North America and Europe emitted the most greenhouse gases. In recent decades, emerging economies such as China and India caught up. By 2017, China emitted twice as much carbon dioxide as the USA and more than four times as much as the European Union. Although, China still emits less carbon dioxide per person than the US.

In 2020, world leaders met in Glasgow, Scotland, and reached the most comprehensive agreement on sustainable development to date. Two hundred nations signed this agreement. China, Russia, and the USA, three of the biggest emitters of carbon dioxide, signed it. The signatories agreed to phase down coal, provide a trillion dollars to support sustainable development in developing countries, stop deforestation within ten years, and cut methane emissions by 30%. The agreement aimed to prevent the average global temperature from rising by more than 1.5 Celsius. India, the world's third-largest emitter of carbon dioxide, was one of the few nations that did not sign the agreement. Although it separately pledged to become carbon neutral by 2070.

Once again, world leaders have promised to reduce emissions and promote sustainable development. Will they stand by their pledges? Unfortunately, global agreements are often not followed. There are a few reasons for this. First, even if governments plan to honor an accord, they often face political resistance at home. For instance, President Biden included several programs in his $1.9 trillion Build Back Better plan designed to promote sustainability. However, his plan initially failed when Senator Joe Manchin, a Democrat from West Virginia, announced that he would not support it. With the Senate split between Democrats and Republicans, Biden needed every Democrat senator to vote in favor of the plan for it to pass. Recently, the US Supreme Court decided that the Environmental Protection Agency could no longer set limits for carbon dioxide emission, an essential tool the federal government had to combat climatic instability.

Even if an administrator manages to ratify an agreement and secures funds to execute it, there is no guarantee that the next administration will follow the plan. For example, President Obama signed the Paris agreement in 2015. However, President Trump chose to withdraw the US from the accord. The US later rejoined the Paris agreement under President Biden, but there is little guarantee of what the next administration would do.

Nations often do not follow international agreements because they lack enforcement. If a county pledges to reduce its emission of greenhouse gases but does not do so, there is no way for other countries to penalize it. Agreements need an enforcement mechanism. For instance, if a county does not meet its emission-reduction goal, other countries should be able to levy a tariff on its imports.

Cooperation over the reduction of greenhouse gases is a social dilemma. In game theory, social dilemmas are situations where individual players can cooperate by taking an action that benefits the group but costs them. The optimal solution is for all the players to cooperate, but the dominant strategy is to defect from the agreement. Since we share the same atmosphere, we will all benefit if every country cuts down its emission of greenhouse gases. However, every country has the incentive to let other countries reduce their emission without making costly adjustments.

Politics over Planet
During the 2020 presidential debate, Biden argued that we shift away from oil to renewable energy by ending subsidies for fossil fuels since they pollute the environment. Trump cleverly retorted by saying, "Basically, what he is saying is he is going to destroy the oil industry. Will you remember that, Texas? Will you remember that, Pennsylvania? Oklahoma? Ohio?" Trump did not attempt to dispute that oil creates pollution. Instead, he tapped into voters' fear of losing their job. 71% of US adults believe that the USA should prioritize alternative energy development over fossil fuels. Nonetheless, they also have other concerns, such as having a job.

During the same debate, Trump claimed that Biden plans to spend $100 trillion on a green new deal. This figure was neither correct nor realistic. Even if Joe Biden wanted to, he could not spend $100 trillion on sustainability when the federal government only collects around $4.4 trillion in taxes. $100 trillion is a scary number. Once again, Trump was shrewdly tapping into people's fears. If we spend $100 trillion on renewable energy, will there be any money left for social security, Medicare, national defense, or education?

Advocates for fossil fuels often look for ways to instill FUD (Fear, Uncertainty, and Doubt) about switching to renewable energy. An example of this FUD technique occurred in February of 2021, shortly after Biden became president. That month three winter storms caused massive blackouts in Texas. The uncommonly cold weather killed over 150 people and created food shortages throughout the state. In an interview with Fox News, Governor Gregg Abbott claimed that the crisis happened because "Our wind and our solar got shut down." Alex Epstein, the author of *The Moral Case for Fossil Fuels*, added, "Had TX been using 100% renewables, we would have had 100% blackouts."

These statements are false. Texas suffered blackouts because it privatized its power sector, disconnected its grid from other states, and relied on faulty gas pipes. The private market is more efficient at providing most products than the government, but this is not the case for electricity. While privatization could lead to competition and lower prices, private energy suppliers have no incentive to build excess capacity. That means that when there is a surge in demand, as there was doing the cold winter of 2020, the private market does not have the capacity to respond.

Texas elected to separate itself from the national grid to avoid federal regulations. Consequently, during the power crisis of 2020, it could not import electricity from other states. Finally, Texas relied on faulty natural gas pipes and did not winterize them. Some of these pipes burst during the winter of 2020.

Governor Abbot blamed renewable energy instead of his poor choices for the 2020 energy crisis. He probably did it to avoid culpability and to support the gas industry. Texas is the largest producer of natural gas in the USA; it produces almost a fourth of the nation's gas. Abbott received about $4.6 million from the gas industry. It was against his political interest to blame gas pipelines for the outages.

The winter crisis in Texas illustrated how politicians twist perceptions. Abbot took a calamity caused by climatic instability and exacerbated by improperly poor decisions and poorly built gas lines and used it to argue that renewable energy was the problem. The crisis demonstrated how powerful the oil lobby is. By donating millions of dollars to political campaigns, the oil lobby gets politicians like Abbot to divert public attention instead of making changes that would benefit their constituents, like investing in sustainable energy.

You Say Natural Gas, I Say Methane

Environmental skepticism is the belief that environmental problems are either untrue or unimportant. Combating skepticism with facts is insufficient and, sometimes, counterproductive. Dale Carnegie explained it best in his seminal book *How to Win Friends and Influence Others*. Carnegie noted that you could rarely convince anyone to change their opinion by hurling facts at them. When someone challenges our long-held beliefs, we dig our heels deeper and come up with counterarguments, no matter how illogical. To gain support for sustainability, we must use descriptive terms and appeal to relevant concerns.

Words can be weapons. Sustainability advocates should convince the media and people to use descriptive terms that accurately illustrate the situation. For instance, the coal industry popularized the term clean coal in 2008. It refers to coal treated with chemicals or washed to reduce its emission. By using this term, the industry not only won public support for coal but also managed to gain additional subsidies from the government.

However, as discussed earlier, clean coal is hardly clean. It emits carbon dioxide and various toxins. Worse, the chemicals used to "clean" the coal are toxic and often end up in local watersheds. Instead, we should use a term like chemically treated coal, which indicates that coal plants use dangerous chemicals to treat the coal and does not suggest that it is harmless to the environment, as the term clean coal implies.

The term natural implies something good, which is why 69% of people worldwide support natural gas and why many people want to live in natural gas communities. The word natural means coming from nature, but according to the Merriam-Webster dictionary, it also implies possessing higher qualities.

What would happen if we call natural gas methane compound instead? After all, up to 90% of natural gas is methane, and the remainder includes dangerous chemicals such as carbon monoxide. How many people would support using methane to produce electricity? How many people would agree to live in methane compound communities? Accurately describing things can lead to change.

Recently, there has been a shift in the media from using the term global warming to using climate change. An article published by NASA explains the reason for this change. "Climate change encompasses global warming but refers to the broader range of changes that are happening to our planet. These include rising sea levels, shrinking mountain glaciers, accelerating ice melt in Greenland, Antarctica, and the Arctic, and shifts in flower/plant blooming times. These are all consequences of warming, caused mainly by people burning fossil fuels and putting out heat-trapping gases into the air."

The term climate change does not convey a sense of urgency. After all, the climate is constantly evolving, and change is not necessarily a bad thing. The sustainability movement should use a more accurate term, like climatic instability. Instability is undesirable. If our climate is becoming increasingly unstable, we must urgently need to do something.

The sustainability movement also needs to appeal to more tangible concerns. The global climate is complex and hard to understand. We cannot see greenhouse gases in the atmosphere. However, there are pertinent reasons why people would want to use fewer fossil fuels. Climatic instability increases the frequency and intensity of hurricanes, floods, droughts, and fires. When these extreme climatic events occur, the media should explain how the greenhouse effect is likely causing them. While the media sometimes refers to climate change during extreme climatic events, it rarely describes how the greenhouse effect leads to these phenomena.

We need to focus on the tangible benefits of renewable energy. As noted previously, renewable energy is domestic and creates local jobs. It reduces our dependence on imports. Its cost is more stable, which means no more paying wildly different prices at the gas pump.

While people might find it hard to understand how solar energy works, they can easily understand the benefits of local jobs.

Similarly, we need to focus on the tangible costs of fossil fuels. Most developed nations have to import oil, natural gas, or coal. Using fossil fuels makes us dependent on imports and also shifts jobs abroad. Some terrorist groups use oil money to support their activities. Lastly, when we purchase fossil fuels, we help empower rogue nations like Russia and Saudi Arabia. People may not understand the impact of fossil fuels on the environment, but they can easily understand the impact of losing local jobs or the threat of terrorism.

We should also combat disinformation, not merely by stating facts about fossil fuels but also by challenging others' thinking. For example, we should question the source of disinformation and ask for evidence. We cannot convince environmental skeptics to stop using fossil fuels and shift to sustainable energy. However, we can help them convince themselves.

The Year the Earth Stood Still

Will the COVID-19 pandemic change people's perspectives about global cooperation and the environment? The pandemic devastated the world, killing over 5 million people in 2020 and 2021. At times, hospitals were overwhelmed with patients. Cities closed down or adjusted their operations to help prevent the spread of the virus. The hospitality, transportation, and retail industries greatly struggled. For the first time in decades, every country in the world was deeply affected by the same issue.

The pandemic also profoundly affected the oil industry. The global energy demand for oil sharply dropped at the start of 2020 as people around the globe were isolated. Oil prices dropped from almost $60 per barrel in 2020 to under $17 by April 2020. Energy investment fell by 18%. World production and gasoline consumption slowed down. The following year, as the US and other countries recovered, oil prices rebounded, rising to over $80 per barrel.

Due to the fall in oil consumption, carbon dioxide emissions dropped steeply in the spring of 2020. In China, the shutdown in February 2020 led to a 25% reduction in carbon dioxide emissions. In Wuhan, where the virus likely originated, strict quarantine requirements halved air pollution. Cities like Los Angles, Jakarta, and New Delhi, which are infamous for their smog, became largely smog-free. With fewer people roaming the streets, animals appeared in towns and unexpected places. Worldwide, carbon dioxide emissions were down by 17%. The effect was only temporary. By 2021, emissions of carbon dioxide rebounded to close to pre-pandemic levels. For a year, the world got a breath of fresh air.

The pandemic served as a reminder about our environmental impact. We saw that even a temporary decrease in industrial production and driving had a noticeable, positive impact on the environment. Humanity also demonstrated an ability to adapt. If people can adapt by working from home, they could also learn to charge their cars at night and rely on sustainable energy.

Most of all, the pandemic reminded us how vulnerable humanity is. A tiny infectious agent, too small to be detected by a conventional microscope, killed millions, shut down schools, and disrupted the global economy. If a microscopic virus can affect humanity so much, imagine how profoundly altering our atmosphere could affect us.

The pandemic reinvigorated the environmental justice movement. According to Pew research, in 2020, 64% of adults in the USA indicated that protecting the environment should be a top priority for the President and Congress. This number was up from 56% in 2019. The environmental movement gained traction in both parties. Ninety percent of all Democrats believe that the government should do more to combat climate, as do 52% of young Republicans (born after 1981).

The pandemic temporarily lowered carbon dioxide emissions and raised support for the sustainability movement. However, it also had negative impacts on the environment. Since the pandemic, consumers have been getting more products delivered to their homes and are using more plastics and cardboard for packaging. They have also been using more masks and gloves. People are getting more takeout food to avoid eating in crowded restaurants, which means they use more packaging material and plastic flatware. Plastic is not biodegradable and can harm marine life if it ends up in the ocean.

The long-term impact of the pandemic on the environment is still unclear. On one hand, the pandemic raised awareness about our dependency on the environment and the importance of global cooperation. Like COVID, climatic instability is a global issue that all countries must collaborate to manage. Additionally, the number of people working from home increased, which means less emission from work commutes. On the other hand, people may be less willing to use public transportation or carpool to work to avoid communicable diseases.

To make meaningful change, we must capitalize on the increasing awareness of environmental sustainability. Countries must invest significant funds in sustainable energy and electric vehicle infrastructure. Build it, and we will use it. Ignore the need to invest in sustainable energy, and our dependence on fossil fuels will continue for many decades and will likely lead to disastrous climatic changes. Unlike COVID, there is no vaccine for climatic instability.

CHAPTER 14: YOU CAN FEEL IT. IT'S ELECTRIC

I look to the future because that's where I'm going to spend the rest of my life. George Burns

Israel seemed like the perfect location to start the EV revolution. Israel is a small country, roughly the size of Massachusetts and slightly smaller than Belgium. Most of its population clusters within a two-hour drive of Tel Aviv, its largest city. Therefore, Israel can serve its entire population with a limited number of charging stations. The country is surrounded by the Mediterranean Sea to the west and Arab nations to the north, south, and east. It is uncommon for Israelis to drive their cars outside their country, where they may not have charging stations. Due to its conflict with several oil-exporting countries and high gasoline tax, gas is costly in Israel, making EVs an appealing alternative. At the start of 2020, gasoline in Israel was $1.78 per litter or $6.74 per gallon. Israel is also one of the most technology-driven nations, and its population is highly adaptable.

When Shai Agassi, an Israeli entrepreneur, developed an EV system called Better Place, it seemed destined to succeed. Better Place utilized battery-swapping stations to make charging quicker. He launched his project in 2007 and raised over $850 million. He was heralded as a visionary and appeared on magazine covers worldwide. His company used a slick-looking Renault. Renault-Nissan agreed to manufacture 100,000 EVs tailored to Better Place's specifications.

Better Place built charging stations around Israel and expanded to Denmark, with plans to expand to other European countries. Better Place seemed on the path to making the world, well, a better place. Numerous people praised the company, but not many people bought its cars. It sold only 750 vehicles and racked up a $500 million debt. In 2013, it shut down. This chapter explains why previous attempts to switch to EVs failed and what we need to do to achieve a sustainable energy economy.

Building a Better Place

Throughout history, automakers have attempted to popularize EVs. The Electrobat, the Fritchle Electric Automobile, the CitiCar, and the EV1 failed. Better Place was another promising EV project that did not gain traction. To ensure that EVs succeed, we must understand why EV schemes like Better Place did not work and what we must do differently.

Better Place did not succeed because its EVs were expensive, inconvenient to drive, and did not match consumers' needs. The company's vehicles retailed for around $35,000, well above the average price for small sedans. They were expensive because they were custom-made, and their batteries cost over $10,000. Better Place also charged $12,000 annually for the first four years of access to the battery-swapping stations. Even in Israel, where gas is pricey, this fee was too steep. Most consumers want to support green technology but are unwilling to pay significantly more.

Better Place's customers could not choose which car to use. Drivers had to use a Renault Fluence. Nissan-Renault-Mitsubishi, a French-Japanese alliance of automakers, manufactured the vehicle. This alliance is the largest producer of EVs. Unfortunately, Fluence was a poor fit for many people. It was too small for large families and too big for some city dwellers given the scarcity of parking in Israeli cities like Tel Aviv and Jerusalem. For consumers to use EVs, automakers must offer a variety of vehicles that meet varying needs.

The biggest obstacle to Better Place was the battery-swap station. To swap batteries, drivers drove their cars over a repair pit. Robotic arms replaced the old battery. The process required the guidance of several people and took at least five minutes. Drivers had to remain in the car during the swap. The number of charging stations was small, and drivers often had to drive out of their way to reach one. To convince consumers to buy EVs, engineers must build many fast and easy-to-use charging stations.

For EVs to thrive, we must convince consumers to purchase them as their primary vehicles. According to a 2018 survey, consumers are most concerned about being unable to charge their EVs on long trips and their prices. About half of those surveyed indicated they were worried about inadequate charging infrastructure.

To switch to EVs, automakers need to produce a variety of affordable EVs, and countries need to develop the infrastructure that will allow drivers to charge their vehicles quickly anywhere. Governments should also subsidize research on battery technology. For instance, we should invest more money in developing affordable solid-state batteries. These batteries use a liquid electrolyte solution. They charge much faster and have a higher capacity than lithium batteries. Unlike lithium batteries, they do not ignite. With solid-state batteries, not only is the car safer to drive but there is no need to have components for fire safety, thus saving space.

What Should Governments Do?

Switching from fossil fuels to sustainable energy is the most challenging and most important public project in history. National and regional governments must take steps to ensure that our future is sustainable. Our economy will not become sustainable without deliberate and extensive government initiative. Governments must take the following actions.

Build EV Charging Stations

Governments must invest considerable funds to help build EV charging stations, sustainable energy infrastructure, and energy storage facilities. Drivers need fast-charging stations for intercity travel. Charging stations are expensive, and until their price significantly goes down, governments should subsidize their production and installation. Commercial chargers range from $2,500 to $7,210 for a Level 2 charger and from $20,000 up to $35,800 for a 50-kilowatt DC fast charger. Charging station owners must invest additional money to connect them to the grid.

Fortunately, the cost of charging stations is decreasing. As with most products, the more charging stations we produce, the cheaper it becomes to build each unit. Governments can encourage the production of charging stations by subsidizing them, providing grants for EV research, and installing charging stations in public facilities. The USA needs about half a million rapid charging stations to allow drivers to charge their EVs no matter where they go. The private market will not install that many charging stations without comprehensive public incentives.

Invest in Sustainable Energy

Governments must also invest heavily in sustainable energy plants, smart grids, and energy storage facilities. The 2010s was a decade of transformation for renewable energy. In 2010, only 4% of the new electric capacity installed was solar. By 2019, the cost of solar power had fallen by 70%, and 40% of the new capacity was solar. US solar energy capacity grew from a gigawatt in 2010 to 86 gigawatts in 2020. The country's wind energy grew from 120 gigawatts in 2010 to 334 gigawatts by the end of that decade.

Solar and wind energy are powering a sustainability evolution, but the transformation is not fast enough. To reach the federal government's goal of having 30% of our electricity generated from renewable energy by 2030, we must install 125 gigawatts of renewable capacity each year. To do so, the federal government must subsidize renewable energy, construct large-scale renewable energy plants, approve new nuclear plants, and issue pro-renewable regulations. State and local governments should provide tax credits for solar panels, zone areas for renewable energy production, and mandate a certain percent of the energy to come from sustainable sources. They should also require developers to build new homes with solar panels, as California recently did.

Governments should also invest in smart electric grids. Smart grids can both distribute and collect energy from multiple points. They encourage homeowners, landowners, and businesses to install solar panels and wind turbines since they can sell excess electricity to the grid. Smart grids allow countries to transfer surplus energy from sunny or windy regions to regions with low energy production.

145

Since most sustainable energy is intermittent, we must store it when there is excess supply and release it when there is excess demand. In 2015, the US had 23 gigawatts (GW) of storage capacity. The most common method of storage, accounting for 96% of stored capacity, was pumped hydroelectricity. However, our ability to build dams is limited, and their reservoirs harm ecosystems. Governments should support the research and development of other technologies, such as compressed air and thermal energy systems. We can also use flywheels, liquefied hydrogen, and biofuels to store energy in cities.

Tax Fossil Fuels

As noted earlier, fossil fuels receive over $400 billion in government subsidies. These subsidies make coal, natural gas, and oil cheaper and make it harder for renewable energies to compete with them. We should eliminate all subsidies for fossil fuels this decade. Additionally, governments must stop supporting the construction of fossil fuel infrastructures such as pipelines and fuel reserves. The USA should also stop using its strategic oil reserves to keep the price of gasoline artificially low. Government support for fossil fuels delays the transition from fossil fuels to sustainable energy.

Ending financial support for fossil fuels is essential but not sufficient. Government should also impose higher taxes on fossil fuels. Europe and Japan are already taxing gasoline heavily. In 2018, the UK levied a $3.49 tax, and Germany had a $2.86 per gallon tax. Japan has a more moderate tax of $1.81 per gallon. By contrast, the US federal government imposes an 18 cents per gallon tax for gasoline and 24 cents for diesel. US states impose an additional gas tax, averaging 29 cents. These taxes are far lower than in most countries.

The USA should substantially increase its tax on gasoline and levy taxes on coal and natural gas. Taxes on fossil fuels discourage their use and generate revenue for sustainable development. Moreover, they force gas companies to internalize the cost of pollution, climatic instability, and environmental degradation caused by fossil fuels. While taxes are unpopular, countries need to increase taxes on gasoline, coal, and gas to shed their dependence on these harmful fuels.

Procure EVs

Governments not only make policies, but they also consume many products. The US federal government owns over 645,000 vehicles. National, state, and local governments manage millions of utility vehicles, police cars, buses, and government-issued cars. If world governments started purchasing EVs instead of gasoline vehicles, they could give the electric revolution an incredible spark.

Since EVs are currently more expensive than gasoline cars, governments would initially spend more money to behave sustainably. The additional cost of an eco-friendly technology is called a green premium. However, EVs could soon be cheaper than gasoline cars. Electric engines have fewer parts, generate less heat, and are easier to maintain than gas engines. Their cost is higher because their battery is expensive, and we currently produce them on a small scale. If we continue to expand EV production, their prices are bound to fall. Eventually, governments will save money by purchasing EVs.

Governments can also use procurement policies to purchase other sustainable products such as bioplastic from corn, asphalt from manure, and sustainable steel forged with electricity. They can also decide to buy electricity from sustainable sources only. If governments want to promote sustainability, they must lead the way by being responsible consumers.

Create a Global Partnership for Sustainability

Finally, governments should sign, honor, and enforce international agreements on sustainability. While every government has its approach to sustainability, international accords may require countries to compromise. All governments must be willing to negotiate in good faith, make compromises, and honor all international agreements on sustainability. Administrations must accept and enforce agreements signed by previous administrations.

They must also be willing to penalize countries that violate international agreements. Without continuity and enforceability, international agreements will not lead to significant results.

We must have international collaboration to address global issues. This collaboration should include supporting sustainable development projects in developing countries, creating a global carbon market, and technology transfers. Wealthy nations must support poorer nations, which do not have the resources to become sustainable. Developed nations can help pay for sustainability projects like preserving the rainforests. They can also train people in developing countries on sustainable practices like installing solar panels and drip irrigation, which is less harmful to the soil. Additionally, they can provide sustainable technology, like genetically modified plants that use less water, to less developed nations for free. These countries need technology transfers to achieve sustainability.

A carbon market allows countries to sell and purchase carbon credits. Countries that exceed their emission-reduction goal can sell credits to countries struggling to meet their goals. A well-designed carbon market awards countries with strong sustainability drives.

What Can You Do?

Governments must lead the drive for sustainability, but everyone should play their part. While many other critical issues affect our lives, such as the rising cost of healthcare, crime, and racism, none is more pivotal than environmental sustainability. Humanity's future rests on our ability to switch from fossil fuels to sustainable energy. Becoming sustainable may seem overwhelming, but there are meaningful things we can all do to support this effort.

Follow the Rs of Resource Management

If you or your kids have been to school recently, you probably heard about the Rs of resource management. You should reduce, reuse, and recycle. Reducing our consumption, reusing products, and recycling help curtail solid waste, but it also helps to reduce our use of fossil fuels. We use energy from fossil fuels to produce things. Moreover, businesses transfer products from factories to distribution centers to sellers. Products often travel long distances before they make it to your home. Trucks, ships, and often trains all use oil.

Many products use petrochemicals such as plastics, nylons, and synthetic fiber. Sellers often wrap products in Styrofoam or bubble paper made from petrochemicals. To reduce your environmental impact, consider purchasing used products and using products for as long as possible. Recycle, repurpose, or donate what you do not use. For example, you can use empty jars as pots for plants or drinking glasses. You can use glass bottles as lamps. Foshbottle.com lists sixty ways you can reuse plastic bottles.

Shop in small stores and try to buy local products. Take reusable bags with you when shopping to avoid using plastic bags. Try buying your produces at a local farmers' market. Ordering things online is convenient, but suppliers use fuel to get the product to your home. While you may not want to do everything listed here, you can start by adopting a few sustainable strategies. As a bonus, acting sustainability will save you money.

Go for the Green

Eco-friendly products usually have a green premium, but they help promote sustainability. You can buy organic products and locally grown vegetables and fruits. You can also eat sustainable meats and avoid beef. Beef is not sustainable since cows consume ample water and release methane when digesting food. You can also use energy-efficient appliances and insulate your home to save energy. Every decision can help support sustainability and serve as an example.

If you want to support sustainability, purchase an EV. You do not have to rush to your nearest Tesla dealer. However, next time you are in the market for a car, consider getting an electric or hybrid vehicle. During this decade, you will see a variety of new EVs by American, European, and Asian automakers. Despite commitments by car producers, they will not continue to produce EVs unless enough consumers buy them. By being an early adopter, you can help support the electric revolution.

Pick a Pocketful of Sunshine.

The US and other governments provide tax incentives to install solar panels. Many US states have additional tax credits. Use Google Project Sunroof to calculate the costs and benefits of purchasing panels. Solar panels are becoming more affordable. With federal and state tax incentives, you will typically recover the cost of installing solar panels within 8 to 12 years, depending on your home type and local climate. Your home insurance policy will likely cover the solar panels if they are attached to your house. Moreover, having panels will raise the value of your home. Installing panels could encourage your neighbors to do the same.

Let's Get Fiscal

Most national governments will not prioritize sustainability without continuous pressure from voters. Politicians usually focus on winning the next election rather than on long-term sustainability. To pressure politicians, you can write to your representatives, donate money to green parties or candidates, or run for office. Do not underestimate the role of local governments. Local governments can compel developers to build sustainable buildings, procure EVs and other sustainable products, and allocate land to sustainable energy. You can also support environmental non-profit organizations like the Union of Concerned Scientists or Friends of the Earth.

Educate Yourself and Others

If sustainability is important to you, keep learning about it and share what you learned. Our knowledge about sustainability and the environment is constantly evolving. Teach your friends, children, or students about sustainability. Use social media to influence others. Sometimes, people's understanding is not wrong, just outdated. For instance, if someone argues that solar energy is too expensive, you can explain that this was true in 2010, but now it is the cheapest source of electricity.

Try to avoid using terms like clean coal and natural gas. These terms are inaccurate—the oil lobby created them to promote fossil fuels. If you get into a discussion with an environmental skeptic, it is usually counterproductive to hurl facts at them. Instead, try to understand their thinking and challenge them with questions. You could ask them if they are worried about oil spills or oil money supporting terrorism. Ask them if they support the energy independence and domestic jobs that renewable energy creates. If you want to win someone over, try to appeal to things that concern them.

Failure is Not an Option

History provides several examples of civilizations that collapsed because they severely degraded their environments. Easter Island is a small, isolated island in the South Pacific. The Rapa Nui people, a Polynesian group, settled on the island around 1200 AD and developed a thriving civilization. However, they gradually deforested the island for agriculture and their religion. They used trees to transport colossal stone statues of human figures known as Moai. The forest enriched the soil and held it together. Deforestation and introducing rats to the island caused their agrarian society to collapse.

The Mayans, a complex ancient civilization, also contributed to their downfall by degrading their environment. The Mayan culture built large cities with tall temples that dominated Central America for centuries. However, starting in 850 AD, Mayans began abandoning their settlements. The prevailing theory is that the Mayans left their cities during a prolonged drought that lasted a century. Many scientists believe that their pervasive agricultural practices, which included deforestation, drying wetlands, and withdrawing water from reservoirs, caused the drought.

History abounds with examples of human-made environmental catastrophes. In the 1920s, expansion of farming into

151

marginal prairie lands and over-tilling destroyed topsoil in the USA. Soil erosion combined with a drought in the early 1930s led to a series of massive dust storms in the Southwest. This phenomenon was called the Dust Bowl. The dust killed hundreds, sickened thousands, and devastated livestock. Many farmers had to abandon their land and look for work in the city. Unfortunately, work was hard to find due to the Great Depression.

We are repeating the mistakes of the past. Fossil fuels degrade the environment, emit pollution, and release greenhouse gases, which lead to climatic instability. The greenhouse effect will significantly affect life on earth. The earth's average temperature will rise between 0.5°F to 8.6°F this century. An increase of one- or two-degrees Fahrenheit will likely have a moderate effect on the world's climate, but a large increase in temperature could be disastrous.

Rising temperatures can cause the ice sheets to melt, causing massive floods in coastal cities such as New York, Miami, Venice, Shanghai, and Tokyo. It will also cause large-scale droughts, massive fires, and more hurricanes. The extent of the damage depends on how sharply and quickly we reduce our use of fossil fuels.

Humanity has reached a fork in the road. We can mass-produce EVs and generate most of our electricity from sustainable energy by the middle of the century. Alternatively, we can ignore the impact of fossil fuels on the environment and continue using them. The sustainable energy path leads to climatic stability, environmental sustainability, and economic prosperity. The fossil fuels path will lead to climatic calamities, environmental degradation, political conflict, and economic instability. It is time for our generation to choose an electric future.

SUMMARY OF PART IV

Switching from fossil fuels to sustainable energy is the most challenging and pivotal undertaking in human history. Governments should fund sustainable energy plants, help build charging stations, purchase green products, and tax fossil fuels. However, it is hard to convince some people that we must stop using fossil fuels since the oil industry has created a campaign of fear, uncertainty, and doubt to produce skepticism about climatic instability. To succeed, we must form a global partnership for sustainability. All the biggest emitters of carbon dioxide supported the most recent accord to achieve carbon neutrality. However, governments might not enforce this agreement without constant pressure from voters. In addition to lobbying your government representatives, you can educate others, buy green products, and repurpose products to minimize waste. Our generation will determine whether our future will be disastrous or electric.

POSTSCRIPT: BACK IN THE U.S.S.R.

You don't know how unlucky we are.

I titled this book *The Future is Electric* because of my optimistic belief that humanity will make wise decisions and switch to sustainable energy. However, switching from fossil fuels to EVs that run on sustainable energy requires an enormous investment. Some governments might be unwilling to make this investment. Moreover, there are organizations, politicians, and countries that greatly benefit from the production and sale of fossil fuels. They will continue to thwart our effort to switch to sustainable energy, even though fossil fuels harm the environment, create climatic instability, and fund nefarious regimes.

As I was about to publish this book, the unthinkable happened. Russia invaded its neighbor, Ukraine, and laid siege to its cities. Millions of women and children fled the country, while most Ukrainian men and many women bravely stayed behind to protect their beloved country. Every day I watched as the Russian military shelled cities, destroyed buildings, and carelessly took the lives of thousands. Vladimir Putin committed unspeakable atrocities with no conceivable justifications. Putin committed the worst atrocities Europe experienced since Hitler unleashed a campaign of terror during World War II.

Ukraine was once a satellite of the Soviet Union. Now, it found itself once more oppressed by Russia. Most countries condemned Russia's actions and instituted economic sanctions against it. The West stopped buying vodka, diamonds, and other Russian products. Companies like McDonald's, Amazon, and Volkswagen withdrew from Russia. Even oil giants like Exxon Mobil halted their Russian operations and stopped buying Russian oil, giving up billions of dollars. The world pressured Russia to discontinue the war by trying to hurt its economy.

The Invasion of Ukraine caused the price of oil and natural gas to rise. Gasoline prices in the USA rose above $4.30, pushing the

USA to its highest inflation since 1981. Once more, our dependence on oil led to economic instability. The price of natural gas in Europe surged from 200 to 600 Euros. Many European countries are so dependent on natural gas from Russia that they have no choice but to continue purchasing it. Europe is inadvertently helping finance the Russian military. In fact, by April of 2022, the European Union gave one billion Euros to support Ukraine while at the same time purchasing 35 billion Euros worth of gas from Russia. Our addiction to fossil fuels helped empower a rogue nation to commit inhumane acts.

As I finish this book, I think about the Ukrainian families whose homes were barbarously destroyed by a military financed by fossil fuels. I think about thousands of people who were tortured, shot, and beheaded by the Islamic State, which funded their ruthless campaign using oil money. I think of our partner university near Bonn, Germany, whose campus was destroyed by unprecedented floods caused by climatic instability. I think of the countless animals that died during the Deep Horizon spill in 2010. I think of the irreparable harm inflicted on the environment when power companies blow up entire mountaintops to search for coal.

Then I think of my newborn son. Would he grow up in a world with fossil fuels or an electric world? Will he drive an EV on highways with many charging stations? When he is an adult, will the climate become more stable since we switched to sustainable energy or increasingly unstable since we are still using fossil fuels? It is up to our generation to ensure that our children's future is electric.

REFERENCES

To see the sources for this book, please open the following document. https://drive.google.com/file/d/1MXrx2wQI1bYdGBxYC6uAx3kwfOp4 xivE/view?usp=sharing